WJEC

AS Physics

Study and Revision Guide

Nigel Wood • Iestyn Morris • Gareth Kelly

Published in 2012 by Illuminate Publishing Ltd, P.O Box 1160,
Cheltenham, Gloucestershire GL50 9RW

Orders: Please visit www.illuminatepublishing.com
or email sales@illuminatepublishing.com

British Library Cataloguing in Publication Data

A catalogue record for this book is available from the British Library

ISBN 978-1-908682-04-8

Printed in England by Lightning Source, Milton Keynes, UK.

The publisher's policy is to use papers that are natural, renewable and recyclable
products made from wood grown in sustainable forests. The logging and manufacturing
processes are expected to conform to the environmental regulations of the country of
origin.

Every effort has been made to contact copyright holders of material reproduced in this
book. If notified, the publishers will be pleased to rectify any errors or omissions at the
earliest opportunity.

This material has been endorsed by WJEC and offers high quality support for the
delivery of WJEC qualifications. While this material has been through a WJEC quality
assurance process, all responsibility for the content remains with the publisher.

Editor: Geoff Tuttle
Cover and text design: Nigel Harriss
Text and layout: The Manila Typesetting Company

Acknowledgements

We are very grateful to the team at Illuminate Publishing for their professionalism,
support and guidance throughout this project. It has been a pleasure to work so closely with them.

The authors and publisher wish to thank:
Len Belton for his thorough review of the book and expert insights and observations.

Helen Francis of WJEC.

Contents

How to use this book

The authors of this book are senior A level Physics examiners. We have written this study guide to help you understand what is required to do well in your studies. The contents of the guide are structured to help you to success in WJEC A level Physics.

There are notes for the externally assessed units:

> PH1 – Motion, Energy and Charge

> PH2 – Waves and Particles

and for the internally assessed unit

> PH3 – Practical Physics

Knowledge and Understanding

The first section of the book covers the key knowledge and skills required for the examination.

In addition, we have given some pointers to help your revision:

- Many Physics terms are defined – you should also refer to the WJEC document 'Terms, Definitions and Units'.

- There are 'Quickfire' questions designed so that you can test your own progress.

- We have given advice based on our experience of what candidates need to do to raise their grades.

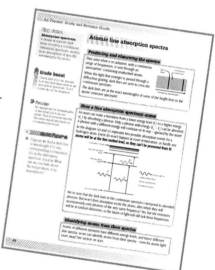

Exam Practice and Technique

The **second section** of the book covers the key skills for examination success and gives examples of candidates' actual responses to past-paper questions. This section also explains about key terms which examiners use when they set questions and how you should respond to them.

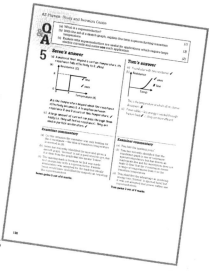

A complete range of question types is given. Each question has two answers of different standards and there is also a commentary to explain why the candidates received the marks they did.

The **practice questions** section which precedes the examination questions has a series of practice questions covering units PH1, PH2 and PH3. These are not past paper questions but are designed to give you pointers in your examination preparation. There are model answers to these questions, i.e. responses which the examiners would consider to be ideal.

The most important thing is that you take responsibility for your own learning and examination preparation. This will include making your own notes as you go through the course and consulting textbooks and other sources. The WJEC website, www.wjec.co.uk, has the specification, guidance notes, past papers and mark schemes. Remember that preparation for examinations is an **active** process – not just reading and learning, but making notes and practising the techniques which you will need to attain the highest possible grade.

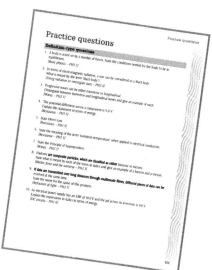

We wish you every success.

Nigel Wood   Iestyn Morris   Gareth Kelly

Knowledge and Understanding

PH1 Motion, Energy and Charge

This module is full of basic physics that is essential and should provide a solid grounding for your future physics career. The first step is to know your units, scalars and vectors – the foundations of measurement. You will then move onto the fundamentals of forces, moments and equilibrium – the essentials of making things move or remain stationary. In kinematics you will progress to actual motion – learn your definitions, understand the intricacies of the motion graphs and then obtain a confident grasp of the constant acceleration equations. These cornerstones lead on naturally to the concepts of terminal velocity and projectile motion. Energy is the boiler house of this module and you will need to be assured when calculating various forms of energy, their conservation and work. Power, efficiency and energy loss are also essential. The second half of the module leads onto electricity where you'll need to understand charging insulators by friction, the concepts of charge and current leading to deriving an expression for current due to a drift velocity. The next topic will be Ohm's law progressing to a definition of resistance – key to all electricity and electronics. Further subtleties of I–V graphs, resistivity and some experiments will follow before an introduction to the hugely important field of superconductivity. Finally, some more intricacies of dc circuits will be explored, initially from principles of conservation of charge and energy leading to potential dividers and internal resistance of cells.

Revision checklist

Tick column 1 when you have completed brief revision notes.

Tick column 2 when you think you have a good grasp of the topic.

Tick column 3 during final revision when you feel you have mastered the topic.

		1	2	3	Notes
p8	**Basic physics**				
p8	Units and dimensions				
p9	Scalars and vectors				
p10	Forces and Newton's laws				
p12	Resolving vectors				
p14	Newton's third law				
p16	Density				
p17	Moments and stability				
p19	Centre of gravity				
p20	**Kinematics**				
p20	Definitions				
p21	Representing motion				
p25	Constant acceleration equations				
p28	Air resistance				
p30	Projectile motion				

Basic physics

Units and dimensions

Although this might not be the most exciting physics, you can't measure anything without first understanding units.

There are six base units that you'll need to know for this course and these relate to the most fundamental and basic properties of physics

Base quantity	Unit	Symbol
Length	metre	m
Mass	kilogram	kg
Time	second	s
Electrical current	ampere	A
Temperature	kelvin (or Celsius)	K (or °C)
Amount of substance	mole	mol

At this stage, you only need to know the first four units and quantities, which need no introduction as you've been using them for years. You'll encounter the kelvin and the mole later (if you haven't encountered them already).

Grade boost

Set your answer out in this way: do LHS then RHS and make a comment, e.g. QED.

≫ Pointer

Remember you only need the units so the 2 (in $2as$) is not needed. Also, you can only add two things together if they have the same units, i.e. u^2 and $2as$ must have the same units.

 quickfire

① Check that the equation $s = ut + \frac{1}{2}at^2$ is homogeneous.

quickfire

② Express the unit of pressure in terms of the SI base units.

quickfire

③ An equation that gives the air resistance force (or drag) is $F = kv^2$. Find the unit of k.

Example

The most common question asked relating to base units is checking that both sides of an equation have the same units – sometimes referred to as checking equations for homogeneity.

Check that the equation $v^2 = u^2 + 2as$ is homogeneous

Answer

Left-hand side (LHS) $\{v^2\} = (m\,s^{-1})^2 = m^2s^{-2}$

Right-hand side (RHS) $\{u^2 + 2as\} = (m\,s^{-1})^2 + m\,s^{-2} \times s = m^2s^{-2} + m^2s^{-2} = m^2s^{-2}$ hence OK or QED if you prefer.

[unit of acceleration]

Example

Another type of question that can be asked is expressing SI units in terms of their base units, e.g. express the unit of power, W (watt) in terms of SI base units.

Answer

You'll need to juggle these three equations:

$$P = \frac{W}{t}, \; W = F \times d, \; F = ma$$

so $\quad P = \dfrac{F \times d}{t} \quad$ and, $\quad P = \dfrac{ma \times d}{t}$

Finally, $\quad [Power]$ or $W = \dfrac{kg \times m\,s^{-2} \times m}{s} = kg\,m^2\,s^{-3}$

Scalars and vectors

All things that you measure in physics are classified as either scalar or vector.

The essential difference between a scalar and a vector is that a vector has direction. This means that adding two scalars is easy, whereas you must use geometry to add two vectors.

Mass is a scalar, so $\quad$ 2 kg + 5 kg = 7 kg

whereas Force is a vector, hence 2 N + 7 N = . . . depends on their directions.

The syllabus says you need to be able to add and subtract vectors – this means you must be able to draw the following type of diagram:

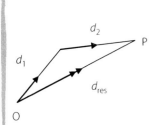

> The diagram on the left shows how to add two displacements d_1 and d_2. Suppose a car starts from O and has a displacement d_1 followed by a displacement d_2. The car ends up at P with a displacement of d_{res}. What you've just done is to add the two vectors d_1 and d_2, giving a resultant displacement of d_{res}. All vectors add up in this way – you do the same for forces, velocities, accelerations, etc.

Here's a list of most of the scalars and vectors you'll encounter in the A level syllabus:

Scalars – density, mass, volume, distance, length, work, energy (all forms), power, charge, time, resistance, temperature, potential (or pd or voltage), capacitance, activity, pressure.

Vectors – displacement, velocity, acceleration, force, momentum, electric field strength, magnetic field strength, gravitational field strength.

NOTE

Distance or **length** are scalars and have no direction – they are just values in metres **without** a direction.

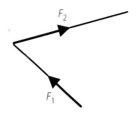

Key Terms

Force = a push or a pull acting on a body from some external body.

Resultant force = the vector sum of forces acting on a body (sometimes the resultant force is called the net force).

Displacement has a direction and is a vector, e.g. a car moves 10m in the direction N30°E.

Speed is a scalar (because it is the rate of change of **distance** and doesn't have a direction).

Velocity is a vector (because it is the rate of change of **displacement** and has a direction).

Acceleration is a vector (because it is the rate of change of **velocity** and has a direction).

Pressure is a scalar (even though it's force/area) because it acts in all directions and it's the area that decides the direction of the force.

Forces and Newton's laws

Forces either push or pull but a far more useful explanation of forces is the following:

UNBALANCED FORCES MAKE THINGS CHANGE VELOCITY

Only six words, but these will give you a good idea of what forces do. One conclusion of the statement is Newton's first law – that things travel at a constant velocity (including velocity = 0) unless you have unbalanced forces. This statement also helps you understand Newton's second law:

$$\Sigma F = ma$$

The equation says that the **resultant force** (ΣF) is equal to the mass × acceleration. Note that balanced forces mean that the resultant force is zero but that unbalanced forces mean we have a non-zero resultant force leading to acceleration (i.e. a [rate of] change of velocity). One way or another you'll be using this equation hundreds of times before the end of the A level course – it's rather useful so get to know it!

Example

Calculate the acceleration of the helicopter [4].

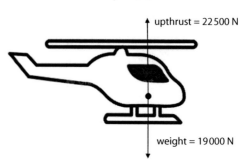
upthrust = 22 500 N
weight = 19 000 N

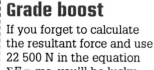

Grade boost

If you forget to calculate the resultant force and use 22 500 N in the equation $\Sigma F = ma$, you'll be lucky to obtain 1 mark out of 4 for using weight = mg. You must realise that the equation $\Sigma F = ma$ refers to the resultant force or suffer the consequences.

Answer

Resultant force = 22 500 − 19 000 = 3500 N   (upwards)   1

But we want to use $\Sigma F = ma$, so we need to know the mass. Can you see the clue in the question? You can calculate the mass of the helicopter from its weight but you'll also need g, the acceleration due to gravity ($9.81\,\mathrm{m\,s^{-2}}$) from the front of the WJEC data booklet (which you take to your examinations).

Weight $= mg = 19\,000$ N   1

so $m = 19\,000 / 9.81 = 1940$ kg

in $\Sigma F = ma$ $\Rightarrow 3500 = 1940 \times a$ 1

finally, $a = \dfrac{3500}{1940} = 1.80\,\mathrm{m\,s^{-2}}$ (upwards)   1

The reason for being able to draw resultant vectors from earlier might seem a bit clearer now – Newton's second law always needs the resultant force. However, you also need to do calculations to obtain the resultant when you have two vectors at right angles. How do you find the resultant force and acceleration for the block shown on the right?

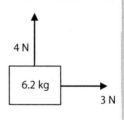

You'll know that this triangle gives the resultant force:

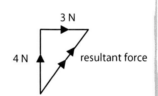

It's often even more helpful to complete the oblong with the resultant as the diagonal

and we need the length of the hypotenuse (which is the diagonal)

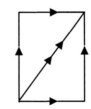

from Pythagoras $h^2 = 4^2 + 3^2 = 16 + 9 = 25$
so, $h = \sqrt{25} = 5$ N

Is this the final answer to the resultant force? No, because examiners, rather sneakily, expect you also to give the direction of the force (since it's a vector). You'll need to label an angle in the diagram and then calculate it:

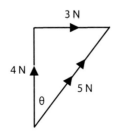

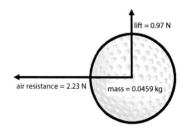

you can use any of the following to calculate θ in the diagram

$$\sin\theta = \frac{3}{5} \quad \text{or} \quad \cos\theta = \frac{4}{5} \quad \text{or} \quad \tan\theta = \frac{3}{4}$$

so, $\quad \theta = \sin^{-1}\left(\frac{3}{5}\right) = \cos^{-1}\left(\frac{4}{5}\right) = \tan^{-1}\left(\frac{3}{4}\right) = 36.9°$

Now, you can calculate the acceleration of the block from

$$\Sigma F = ma \quad \Rightarrow \quad 5 = 6.2a \quad \therefore \quad a = \frac{5}{6.2} = 0.806 \, \text{m s}^{-2}$$

It's also important to repeat here the correct conclusion for this section:

THE ACCELERATION IS ALWAYS IN THE SAME DIRECTION AS THE RESULTANT FORCE

quickfire

⑩ Calculate the horizontal and vertical components in the following:

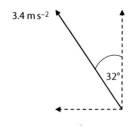

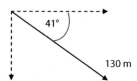

Resolving vectors into different directions

Unfortunately, vectors don't usually have the direction that you want them to have. Take the example:

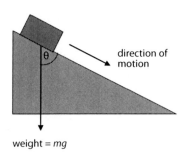

weight = mg

As the block slides down the slope, the force of gravity (weight) acts downwards but the block must move along the slope which is in a different direction. You need to calculate the part of the gravitational force (weight) that acts in the direction of the slope. This is very similar to calculating the resultant of two vectors but in reverse. The diagram below shows what you're trying to do.

quickfire

⑪ The horizontal component of the electric field, E, is given. Calculate E and its vertical component.

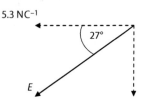

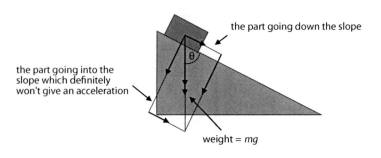

The two vectors that have been drawn give a resultant vector which is the weight (the oblong has been completed as in a similar earlier example). The clever bit about this process is that we can use the bit going down the slope to calculate an acceleration (the other bit just pushes the block into the slope).

The correct terminology for this process is **resolving** the **vector** (weight) into two components (down the slope and into the slope).

All you have to do now is the actual calculation. If you look at the diagram, you'll see that

$$\cos \theta = \frac{a}{h} = \frac{F_{\text{down the slope}}}{mg}$$

rearranging gives

$$F_{\text{down the slope}} = mg\cos \theta$$

Now, suppose $\theta = 60°$ and that the block is on an air track so that there is practically no friction, you can use the equation for Newton's second law and take the resultant force as $mg\cos \theta$

$$\Sigma F = ma$$

$$\cancel{m}g\cos \theta = \cancel{m}a$$

the two m cancel $\quad a = g\cos \theta = 9.81 \times \cos 60 = 9.81 \times 0.5 = 4.91 \text{ m s}^{-2}$

(for the Jeremy Clarksons among you, 4.91 m s^{-2} corresponds to 0–60 mph in around 5.5 s).

A similar example that examiners use regularly is pulling a sled.

Example

Calculate the horizontal component of the force exerted on the sled.

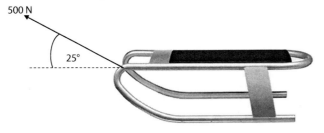

Answer

$500 \times \cos 25 = 453 \text{ N}$

(if you prefer, $\cos 25 = \frac{a}{h} = \frac{F_{\text{horizontal}}}{500} \quad \Rightarrow \quad F_{\text{horizontal}} = 500\cos 25$

Another very popular type of question is resolving velocities into vertical and horizontal components.

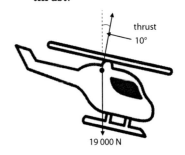

quicKfire

⑫ The vertical component of the helicopter thrust is equal to its weight. Calculate the helicopter's thrust.

thrust
10°
19 000 N

quicKfire

⑬ In the last helicopter question, calculate the helicopter's horizontal acceleration. (Hint: you'll need to find its mass first, see the first helicopter example.)

Pointer

Know your geometry because you might be resolving vectors or finding resultants three times on the PH1 paper - in a force question, a moment question and in a projectile question.

Newton's third law = If a body **A** exerts a force on a body **B**, then **B** exerts an equal and opposite force on **A**.

Example

Resolve the velocity shown into its vertical and horizontal components.

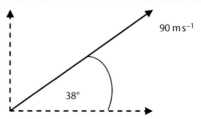

$90\,\mathrm{m\,s}^{-1}$

$38°$

Answer

$$v_{horizontal} = 90\cos 38 = 70.9\,\mathrm{m\,s}^{-1} \qquad \text{since} \qquad \cos 38 = \frac{a}{h} = \frac{v_{horizontal}}{90}$$

$$v_{vertical} = 90\sin 38 = 55.4\,\mathrm{m\,s}^{-1} \qquad \text{since} \qquad \sin 38 = \frac{o}{h} = \frac{v_{vertical}}{90}$$

This whole process may seem a bit pointless now – you start off with one vector, you do a bit of geometry and then you end up with two different vectors. How does that simplify things? It turns out that the only way to solve many problems is to resolve vectors in different directions. After all, could you have calculated the acceleration of the block down the air track without resolving the force vector?

For the moment, the best thing to do is to practise and to treat this as a boring mathematical exercise.

Grade boost

Sometimes it can be difficult to identify the pair of forces in Newton's third law but it's easier than you think. All you have to do is swap the objects around and say 'equal and opposite', e.g. a **tractor** pulls a **trailer** – so its pair force is 'a **trailer** pulls a **tractor** with an equal and opposite force'.

quickfire

⑭ Describe the forces that are equal and opposite to those shown according to Newton's third law.

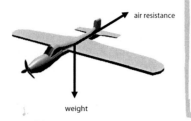

air resistance

weight

Newton's third law

This law concerns forces when one thing exerts a force on another (see the key term). Take as an example a hockey stick hitting a ball.

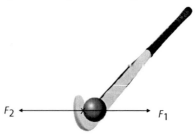

F_2 ← → F_1

In this case, body A is the stick and body B is the ball. So, the stick exerts a force on the ball (F_1). Newton's third law tells you that the ball must exert an equal and opposite force on the stick (F_2). In case you don't believe this force F_2 exists, just look at the dents in a used hockey stick (or cricket bat), some force must be causing these.

If you'd like a quick demonstration of Newton's third law just kick a brick wall. Your foot will exert a force on the wall but the wall will exert a force on your foot (hence the pain). These two forces will be equal and opposite.

Difficult example

A box sits on a table. Give the Newton's third law equal and opposite force to each of the two named forces (weight and normal contact force).

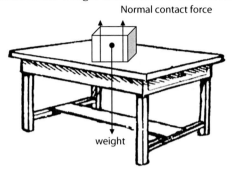

Answer

1 The normal contact force = the table pushes up on the box. So the equal and opposite force to this is that the box pushes down on the table (these are in fact electromagnetic forces due to the atoms in the box and the table being slightly squashed).

2 The weight = the Earth exerts a gravitational force downwards on the box. So the equal and opposite force to this is the box exerts a gravitational force upwards on the Earth.

Don't fall into the following trap – the weight is equal and opposite to the normal contact force so they are a pair of Newton's third law forces. This might, at first glance, seem sensible but is incorrect. There are three rules that must be obeyed:

1 The forces act on different bodies.

2 The forces are equal but in opposite directions.

3 The forces are the same type, e.g. both contact forces or both gravitational forces, etc.

Free body diagrams

These are simplified diagrams showing the forces acting on an object.

Example

Draw **a free body diagram** for a submarine, showing the four following forces: drag, buoyancy, weight and thrust.

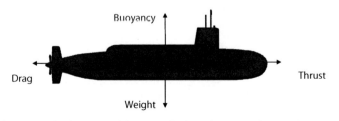

Note, a box is perfectly acceptable instead of a submarine shape. Also, you don't have to be familiar with the terms drag (water resistance in this case) or buoyancy.

 quickpire

⑮ An accelerating car on a flat road experiences the following five forces: driving force, friction, air resistance, weight and normal reaction force from the road. Draw a free body diagram for the car.

Grade boost

To obtain full marks, you will need to ensure that the lengths of the arrows are consistent, e.g. for the accelerating car above, the weight arrow should be the same length as the normal reaction arrow. Also, the driving force arrow should be slightly longer than the friction + air resistance arrows.

$$\text{Density} = \frac{mass}{voume} \quad \text{Unit: kg m}^{-3}$$

the mass and volume apply to any sample of the material.

≫ **Pointer**

Wires come up regularly in A-level physics. Remember that a wire is a long cylinder so,

$$\text{Area} = \pi r^2 = \pi \frac{d^2}{4},$$

$$\text{Volume} = \pi r^2 \times length$$

$$= \pi \frac{d^2}{4} \times length$$

Density

This is the property of a material that gives us the concentration of its mass. The density of a material is a constant and does not depend on the size and shape of the sample of material. Take gold, for instance, gold has a higher density than water, which has a higher density than air. In fact, the density of gold = 19 300 kg m^{-3} i.e. the mass of 1 cubic metre of gold is 19.3 tonnes (1 tonne = 1000 kg). The density of water is 1000 kg m^{-3} i.e. a cubic metre of water has a mass of 1 tonne and the density of air is around 1.2 kg m^{-3} (that's right, air isn't quite as light as you might have thought – a cubic metre of air has a mass of around 1.2 kg).

Another common unit that is used for density is g cm^{-3}. How do you convert from kg m^{-3} to g cm^{-3}?

The easiest way is to remember that 1 kg = 1000 g and 1 m = 100 cm

hence, $\quad$ 1 kg m^{-3} = 1000 g × (100 cm)$^{-3}$ = 1000 × (100)$^{-3}$ g cm^{-3}

$$= \frac{1000}{100 \times 100 \times 100} \text{ g cm}^{-3} = \frac{1}{1000} \text{ g cm}^{-3}$$

so gold density = 19.3 g cm^{-3}, water density = 1 g cm^{-3} etc.

The equation for density as it appears on the WJEC data booklet is:

$$\rho = \frac{m}{V}$$

Example

A student places an empty measuring cylinder on scales and presses the tare (zero) button. After adding 8.0 cm^3 of a liquid to the measuring cylinder, the scales read 8.88 g. Calculate the density of the liquid.

quickfire

⑯ The density of air in a room is 1.25 kg m^{-3} and the air in the room has a mass of 70 kg. Calculate the volume of the room.

Answer

$$\rho = \frac{m}{V} = \frac{8.88}{8.0} = 1.11 \text{ g cm}^{-3} \qquad \text{or (1110 kg m}^{-3}\text{)}$$

Example

The diameter of a platinum wire is 0.254 mm and its length is 6.5 cm. Calculate its mass (platinum density = 21.45 g cm^{-3}).

$$\rho = \frac{m}{V} \quad \Rightarrow \quad m = \rho V$$

Grade boost

You need to be good at converting units – examiners are evil beasts who like to give you data in mixed units. The easiest way in this question is to convert 0.254 mm to cm (i.e. 0.0254 cm).

but for a wire $\quad V = \pi r^2 \times length = \pi \frac{d^2}{4} \times length = \pi \frac{.0254^2}{4} \times 6.5 = 3.29 \times 10^{-3} \text{cm}^{-3}$

hence, $\qquad m = \rho V = 21.45 \times 3.29 \times 10^{-3} = 0.071 \text{g (or 71 mg)}$

Moment – the turning effect of a force

Not only can forces make objects accelerate but they can also make objects rotate. At AS level you'll only encounter rotation about an axis (but it will sometimes be called a hinge or a pivot, etc.). An easy example of calculating a moment is:

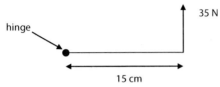

Answer

moment = force × perpendicular distance = 35 × 15 cm = 35 × 0.15 = 5.25 N m

A more difficult example would involve a little bit of geometry:

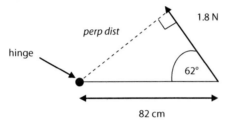

Answer

You need to obtain the perpendicular distance using $\sin 62°$.

$$\sin 62° = \frac{perp\ dist}{82} \quad \Rightarrow \quad perp\ dist = 82 \times \sin 62°$$

Finally, moment = $1.8 \times 0.82 \times \sin 62° = 1.30$ N m

Note that the 82 cm has been changed to 0.82 m to obtain the standard SI unit of N m.

The principle of moments

This principle is used when a system is in equilibrium. You already know that an object cannot be in equilibrium unless the resultant force = 0 (otherwise it would accelerate). But there's another highly useful condition, too, the resultant moment = 0 for an object in equilibrium (otherwise the object would rotate quicker and quicker). These two conditions will give you a lot of information when an object (or a system) is in equilibrium. Also, they will provide many of the tricky questions that appear on the PH1 exam paper and the PH3 experimental paper.

A favourite question is to name the conditions required for a body to be in equilibrium.

Answer

resultant force = 0 **and** resultant moment = 0 (about any point).

Key Terms

Moment about an axis = force × perpendicular distance from the axis.

Principle of moments = for a system in equilibrium, the resultant moment = 0.

Grade boost

Note that the lengths in cm have been changed to m to obtain the standard SI unit of N m. This is not always essential but is usually good practice in order to avoid confusion in units.

Pointer

Although it's easier to remember the principle of moments as resultant moment = 0, you'll always be doing problems where you'll be equating

Σ clockwise moments = Σ anticlockwise moments

quickfire

⑰ Name the two conditions required for a body (or system) to be in equilibrium.

Typical difficult moments exam question

Below is a diagram of a pub sign

(i) Draw arrows on the above diagram indicating the individual weights of the bar and the sign. [2]

See the two downward arrows from the centres of the sign and bar and note that the arrow for the weight of the sign is longer than that of the bar.

(ii) By taking moments about the pivot, apply the principle of moments to the bar and hence calculate T, the tension in the wire. [4]

sum of clockwise moments = sum of anticlockwise moments

$$T \times 1.2 \times \sin 27° = 7.6 \times 0.6 + 14.5 \times 1.2$$

$$T = \frac{7.6 \times 0.6 + 14.5 \times 1.2}{1.2 \times \sin 27°}$$

$$T = 40.3\,\text{N}$$

(iii) Calculate the horizontal force exerted by the pivot on the metal bar. [2]

using resultant horizontal force = 0

$$\text{Force} = T \times \cos 27° = 40.3 \times \cos 27° = 35.9\,\text{N}$$

Remember: there will usually be around 10 marks on the PH1 paper for a question based on moments. Also, there are usually 8 marks (but sometimes 24 marks) on the PH3 paper for a question based on moments (balancing rulers).

Centre of gravity

This, effectively, is where the gravitational force acts on a body. In all cases that you will come across (for AS level) the **centre of gravity** will be at the centre of the body (what is known as the centre of mass). You'll need to know how to find the centres of simple shapes of uniform density, e.g. the bar and pub sign in the last question. Also, for cylinders, spheres and cuboids:

Key Term

Centre of gravity = the point where the entire weight of the body is considered to act.

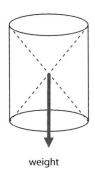

weight

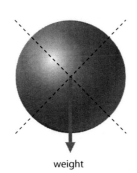

weight

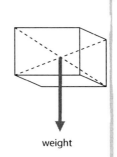

weight

Other than the type of question asked in the pub sign example, about the only other type of question that can be asked relates to objects toppling and stability.

Example
A block (cuboid) rests on a slope that is gradually increased until the cylinder topples. At what angle (θ) does this occur?

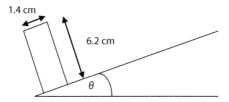

Answer
The block topples when the centre of gravity is directly above its bottom left corner see below.

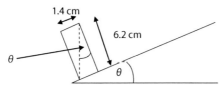

Looking carefully at the diagram $\tan \theta = \dfrac{1.4}{6.2} \Rightarrow \theta = \tan^{-1}\dfrac{1.4}{6.2} = 12.7°$

Finally, for this section, you should be able to quote the following when asked – what are the conditions for a body to be in equilibrium?

Answer: resultant force = 0 **and** resultant moment = 0

Key Terms

Displacement = The displacement of a point B from a point A is the shortest distance from A to B, together with the direction, i.e.

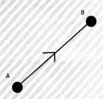

Mean speed =

$$\frac{\text{total distance travelled}}{\text{total time taken}}$$

Mean velocity =

$$\frac{\text{total displacement}}{\text{total time taken}}$$

Mean acceleration =

$$\frac{\text{change in velocity}}{\text{total time taken}}$$

Instantaneous speed = rate of change of distance

Velocity = rate of change of displacement

Acceleration = rate of change of velocity

quickfire

⑱ The car travelling in a circle at constant speed is accelerating. What is providing the resultant force?

Kinematics

Definitions

An essential first step in this topic is knowing and understanding your key terms relating to displacement, speed, velocity and acceleration. The following example of a car travelling around a circular track at a constant speed should provide a good test of your understanding of these terms.

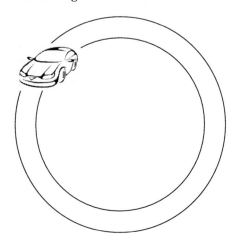

Question

The length of the circular lap shown is 3.6 km and the car completes one circuit at a **constant speed** in 80s. Explain the motion of the car in terms of distance travelled, displacement, speed, velocity, acceleration and their means.

Answer

$$\textbf{Mean speed} = \frac{\text{total distance travelled}}{\text{total time taken}} = \frac{3600}{80} = 45\,\text{m s}^{-1}$$

This is also the instantaneous speed because the car's speed is a constant, i.e. $45\,\text{m s}^{-1}$.

The displacement of the car after one lap is zero (it's back where it started).

So, $\quad\textbf{mean velocity} = \dfrac{\text{total displacement}}{\text{total time taken}} = \dfrac{0}{80} = 0$

This may seem surprising at first glance but it makes sense – the car has no overall displacement so its mean velocity must be zero.

However, things are completely different for the instantaneous velocity. The magnitude of the instantaneous velocity of the car is a constant ($45\,\text{m s}^{-1}$) but its direction is changing continuously. So although the speed is a constant, the **velocity** is changing continuously.

How about the **mean acceleration**? You need to calculate:

$$\text{Mean acceleration} = \frac{\text{change in velocity}}{\text{total time taken}}$$

But after a whole lap the car is in the same place travelling in the same direction with the same speed (45 m s^{-1}). So the velocity at the end of the lap is the same as at the start and the change in velocity $= 0$. So the mean acceleration is also zero.

But the story's different for the instantaneous acceleration which is the rate of change of velocity. The car is accelerating because the velocity is changing (due to the changing direction of the velocity). However, you won't be able to calculate the instantaneous acceleration until module PH4 next year (it's actually around 3.5 m s^{-2}).

This, again, may seem surprising because you might previously have thought that constant speed means no acceleration but this is not true unless the motion is in a straight line. You must realise that it's constant velocity that means no acceleration.

Graphical representation of motion

The syllabus states clearly that you should be able to draw and understand graphs of displacement, velocity and acceleration versus time. These questions can often be quite tricky but if you know your basics, you should be able to gain very high marks.

Displacement–time graph

The important thing to remember with this type of graph is that the gradient is the velocity, i.e. the steeper the graph, the higher the velocity. Remember, gradient is a measure of how quickly y is varying with respect to x (or $\frac{dy}{dx}$ in calculus). In this graph then, the gradient is a measure of how quickly displacement is varying with respect to time, i.e. velocity.

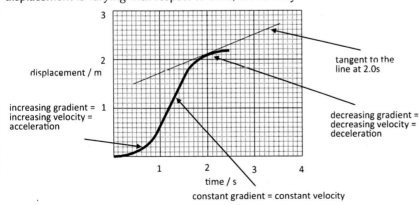

displacement / m

tangent to the line at 2.0s

increasing gradient = increasing velocity = acceleration

decreasing gradient = decreasing velocity = deceleration

time / s

constant gradient = constant velocity

Questions

1. Calculate the velocity between 0.9s and 1.6s.
2. Write down an estimate of the final velocity (at 2.45s) and initial velocity.
3. Calculate the mean acceleration for the first 0.9s.
4. Estimate the velocity at 2.0s.

Answers

1. Between 0.9s and 1.6s, the displacement goes from 0.45 m to 1.80 m, i.e. displacement $= 1.80 - 0.45 = 1.35$ m

   so, $velocity = \dfrac{displacement}{time} = \dfrac{1.35}{0.7} = 1.9\,\text{m s}^{-1}$

2. Zero and zero (because the line is flat i.e. gradient $= 0$).

3. $Acceleration = \dfrac{change\ in\ velocity}{time} = \dfrac{1.9}{0.9} = 2.1\,\text{m s}^{-2}$

4. First you need to draw the tangent to the line at time 2.0s (see the graph). This will give you the gradient of the line at 2.0s. Now, you need to calculate the gradient of the tangent.

   $$gradient = \frac{y_2 - y_1}{x_2 - x_1} = \frac{2.7 - 1.5}{3.5 - 1.4} = \frac{1.2}{2.1} = 0.57\,\text{m s}^{-1}$$

   so, the velocity at 2.0s is 0.57 m s^{-1}.

⑲ For the graph shown:

(i) Describe the motion between 0 and 0.09 s.

(ii) Calculate the velocity between 0.175 s and 0.240 s.

(iii) Calculate the acceleration between 0.09 s and 0.175 s.

(iv) Calculate the deceleration between 0.240 s and 0.330 s.

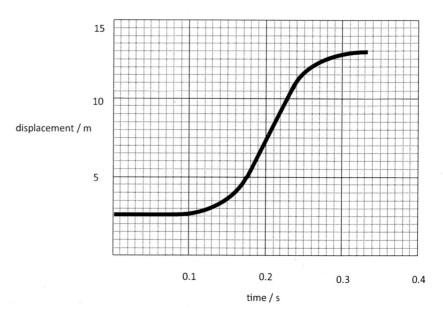

Velocity–time graph

This is the most common graph to appear in exam questions. Now, there are two extremely important points to remember:

1. The gradient of the line is the acceleration (because the gradient is how quickly the velocity is changing with respect to time).

2. The area between the line and the x-axis gives the displacement (or distance travelled).

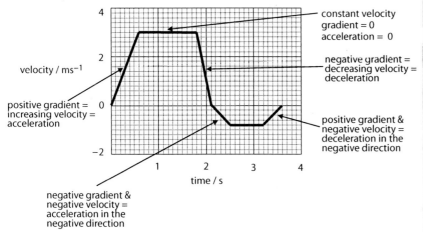

Questions

1. Calculate the acceleration for the periods 0–0.6s, 0.6–1.8s, 1.8–2.1s, 2.1–2.5s, 2.5–3.2s, 3.2–3.6s.

2. Calculate the distance travelled for the period 0–3.6s.

Answers

0–0.6s, $\quad$ acceleration $= \dfrac{\text{change in velocity}}{\text{total time taken}} = \dfrac{3}{0.6} = 5\,\text{m s}^{-2}$

0.6–1.8s, $\quad$ acceleration $= 0$ (constant velocity)

1.8–2.1s, $\quad$ acceleration $= \dfrac{\text{change in velocity}}{\text{total time taken}} = \dfrac{-3}{0.3} = -10\,\text{m s}^{-2}$

2.1–2.5s, $\quad$ acceleration $= \dfrac{\text{change in velocity}}{\text{total time taken}} = \dfrac{-0.8}{0.4} = -2\,\text{m s}^{-2}$

2.5–3.2s, $\quad$ acceleration $= 0$ (constant velocity)

3.2–3.6s, $\quad$ acceleration $= \dfrac{\text{change in velocity}}{\text{total time taken}} = \dfrac{0.8}{0.4} = 2\,\text{m s}^{-2}$

2 Distance travelled = area between the x-axis and the line.

This area can be split up in many ways but the simplest is to consider two trapeziums (0–2.1s and 2.1–3.6 s).

0–2.1s $\quad$ Area $= \dfrac{1}{2}(2.1+1.2)+3 = 4.95\,\text{m}$

2.1–3.6s   Area $= \dfrac{1}{2}(1.5 + 0.7) \times 0.8 = 0.88 \, m$

However, the second area is below the x-axis which is a negative area. Hence the total area (or the distance travelled) is

$$4.95 - 0.88 = 4.07 \, m$$

Acceleration–time graph

The important thing to remember about this graph is that the area between the line and the x-axis gives the velocity (strictly the change in velocity).

Often, you are required to plot an acceleration–time graph after you've been given a velocity–time graph. With that in mind, plot a graph of acceleration–time for the last example (velocity–time graph).

All you have to do is transfer the values of acceleration from the last question.

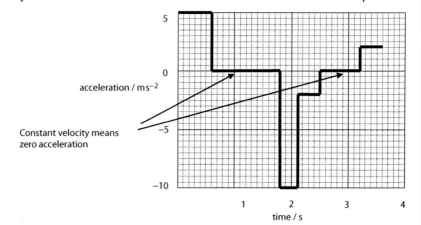

Constant velocity means zero acceleration

acceleration / m s⁻²

time / s

Note: this is the standard shape of the acceleration–time graph for exams. The acceleration is a series of flat constant values.

Questions

1. Use the graph to confirm that the velocity after 0.6s is 3 m s⁻¹.
2. Show that the velocity after 2.1s is zero.

Answers

1. The velocity change is the area between the line and the x-axis from 0–0.6s.

$$\text{Area} = 0.6 \times 5 = 3 \, m\,s^{-1} \quad \text{QED}$$

2. Now you need the area between the line and the x-axis from 0–2.1s.

from 0–0.6s,	Area $= 3 \, m\,s^{-1}$
from 0.6–1.8s,	Area $= 0$
from 1.8–2.1s,	Area $= -10 \times 0.3 = -3 \, m\,s^{-1}$
	Total area $= 3 - 3 = 0 \quad$ QED

Constant acceleration equations

These are four equations that come up time and again linking the following five variables:

x = distance travelled

u = initial velocity

v = final velocity

a = acceleration (this must be a constant!)

t = time

Here are the four equations as they appear on the WJEC data sheet:

$$v = u + at$$

$$x = \frac{1}{2}(u + v)t$$

$$x = ut + \frac{1}{2}at^2$$

$$v^2 = u^2 + 2ax$$

One thing to remember here is that the syllabus says you must be able to derive these equations but this is quite easy. All you need is the following graph and a little bit of algebra.

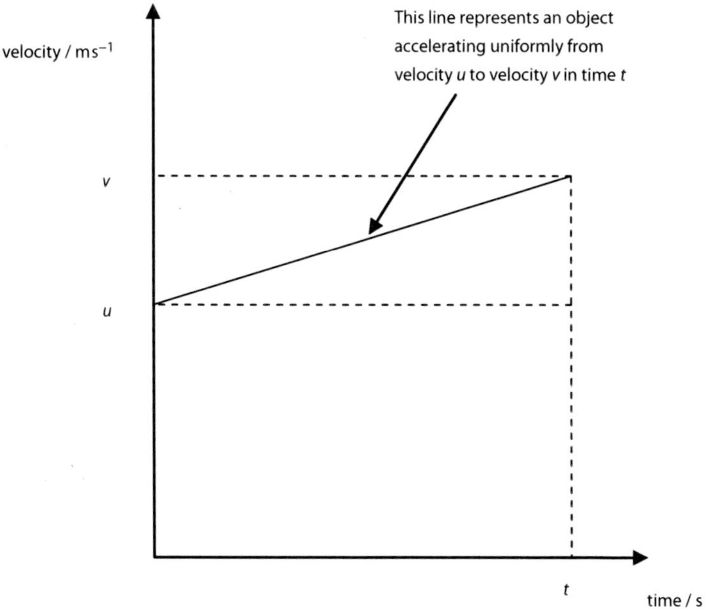
velocity / ms−1
This line represents an object accelerating uniformly from velocity u to velocity v in time t
v
u
t
time / s

quickfire

⑳

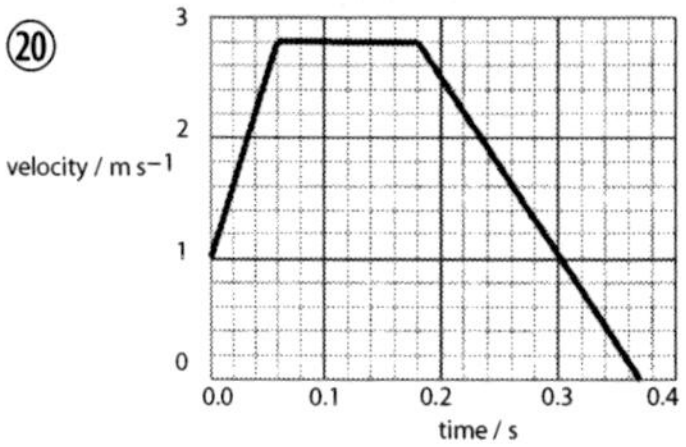
velocity / m s−1
3
2
1
0
0.0
0.1
0.2
0.3
0.4
time / s

For the above graph:

(i) Plot a graph of acceleration against time.

(ii) Calculate the total distance travelled.

Grade boost

When doing algebra, if you substitute for one variable, that's the variable that disappears in the resulting equation.
E.g. sub for v in $v^2 = u^2 + 2ax$ and you'll get the equation without v in it.

quickfire

㉑ Substitute $v = u + at$ into the equation $v^2 = u^2 + 2ax$ and then do some algebra to obtain $x = ut + \frac{1}{2}at^2$.

The first two equations are easily derived by obtaining the gradient and the area between the line and the x-axis.

$$\text{gradient} = \text{acceleration} = \frac{v-u}{t} \Rightarrow a = \frac{v-u}{t} \Rightarrow at = v-u$$

finally,

$$v = u + at \qquad \qquad \text{eq 1}$$

$$\text{Area} = \text{Area of trapezium below the line} = \frac{1}{2}(u+v)t$$

finally, $\quad$ Area = distance travelled $\therefore x = \frac{1}{2}(u+v)t \qquad$ eq 2

Equation 2 can also be interpreted as distance = mean speed × time because the mean speed is $\frac{1}{2}(u+v)$.

The other two equations just require a bit of manipulation of the two equations you've already derived.

Now, substitute $v = u + at$ in equation 2:

$$x = \frac{1}{2}(u+v)t = \frac{1}{2}(u+[u+at])t$$

$$x = \frac{1}{2}(2u+at)t$$

$$x = ut + \frac{1}{2}at^2 \qquad \qquad \text{eq 3}$$

Finally, you need an equation without t in it ($v^2 = u^2 + 2ax$) so you need to substitute for t,

The easiest equation to use is: $v = u + at \Rightarrow t = \frac{v-u}{a}$

Now substitute t in one of the other two equations:

$$x = \frac{1}{2}(u+v)t \qquad \qquad \text{or,} \qquad x = ut + \frac{1}{2}at^2$$

$$x = \frac{1}{2}(u+v)\frac{v-u}{a} \qquad \qquad x = u\frac{v-u}{a} + \frac{1}{2}a\left(\frac{v-u}{a}\right)^2$$

$$ax = \frac{1}{2}(u+v)(v-u) \qquad \qquad ax = u(v-u) + \frac{1}{2}(v-u)^2$$

$$ax = \frac{1}{2}(uv - u^2 + v^2 - uv) \qquad \qquad ax = uv - u^2 + \frac{1}{2}(v^2 - 2uv + u^2)$$

$$ax = \frac{1}{2}(v^2 - u^2) \quad \longleftarrow \qquad ax = uv - u^2 + \frac{1}{2}v^2 - uv + \frac{1}{2}u^2$$

$$2ax = v^2 - u^2$$

$$ax = \frac{1}{2}v^2 - \frac{1}{2}u^2 \text{ etc.}$$

◉◀◀◀◀◀ **quickfire**

㉒ There is in fact a fifth equation which is not usually used and it's an equation without u in it. Substitute $u = v - at$ into $x = ut + \frac{1}{2}at^2$ and see

what you get.

and finally, $v^2 = u^2 + 2ax$ eq 4

Remember, you derive the first two equations using the gradient and the area of the graph and the other two using algebra.

These constant acceleration equations are very useful and can give you some extremely interesting results, especially when you start looking at the motion of projectiles. Unfortunately, they also provide the examiner with an endless source of tricky questions. The only way to make sure you gain good marks in these questions is to practise.

Examples

1. Usain Bolt accelerates uniformly from rest to 13 m s^{-1} in 4.0 s. Calculate his acceleration.

2. A Formula 1 car decelerates uniformly from 100 m s^{-1} to rest in 175 m. Calculate the time taken to stop the car.

3. A netball is dropped from rest from a height of 15 m. Calculate its speed when it hits the ground.

4. A ball is thrown vertically upwards with a velocity of 22 m s^{-1}. Calculate the distance it has travelled after 1.5 s.

5. A cricket ball is thrown upward with an initial vertical velocity of 28 m s^{-1}. Calculate the greatest height it reaches and the time the ball takes to reach the ground again.

Answers

1. Using $v = u + at \Rightarrow a = \dfrac{v - u}{t}$

$$a = \frac{13 - 0}{4} = 3.26 \text{ ms}^{-2}$$

$x =$	$u = 0$
$v = 13$	$a = ?$
$t = 4$	

2. Using $x = \dfrac{1}{2}(u + v)t \Rightarrow t = \dfrac{2x}{u + v}$

$$t = \frac{2 \times 175}{100 + 0} = 3.5 \text{ s}$$

$x = 175$	$u = 100$
$v = 0$	$a =$
$t = ?$	

3. Using $v^2 = u^2 + 2ax = 0 + 2 \times 9.81 \times 15 = 294.3$

$$v = \sqrt{294.3} = 17.2 \text{ m s}^{-1}$$

$x = 15$	$u = 0$
$v = ?$	$a = -9.81$
$t =$	

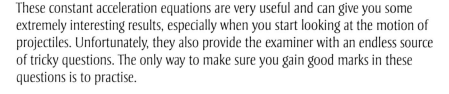

Grade boost

Remember that the gravitational acceleration $g = 9.81$ m s^{-2} can be used whenever you need the vertical motion.

Grade boost

Be careful when things are not in the same direction. In 4 and 5, the initial velocity is upward but the acceleration is down. On this occasion, up was taken as positive so that a became -9.81 m s^{-2}.

» Pointer

Unless you can see immediately how to get the answer, do this, i.e. write what you know. If you know 3 of the variables you can get the others.

Grade boost

Many candidates lose marks in these types of questions for incorrect algebra. Practising with these equations will improve your algebra, too.

≫ Pointer

Sometimes information is hidden in the question. When the ball arrives at its greatest height $v = 0$.

≫ Pointer

Again, some hidden information. When the ball returns to ground level $x = 0$ but there are alternatives. You could take $v = -28$ ms^{-1}. You could also calculate the time taken to reach the highest point and multiply this by 2.

4. Using $x = ut + \dfrac{1}{2}at^2$

$x = 22 \times 1.5 + \dfrac{1}{2}(-9.81) \times 1.5^2$

$x = 33 - 11 = 22\,\text{m}$

$x = ?$	$u = 22$
$v =$	$a = -9.81$
$t = 1.5$	

5. Using $v^2 = u^2 + 2ax$

$0 = 28^2 + 2 \times (-9.81)x$

$2 \times 9.81x = 28^2$

$x = \dfrac{28^2}{2 \times 9.81} = 40\,\text{m}$

$x = ?$	$u = 28$
$v = 0$	$a = -9.81$
$t =$	

for the time $\quad x = ut + \dfrac{1}{2}at^2$

$0 = 28t - \dfrac{1}{2}9.81t^2$

$\dfrac{1}{2}9.81t^2 = 28t$

$\dfrac{1}{2}9.81t = 28 \Rightarrow t = \dfrac{2 \times 28}{9.81} = 5.7\,\text{s}$

$x = 0$	$u = 28$
$v =$	$a = -9.81$
$t = ?$	

Air resistance

So far, you've been solving motion problems without taking account of air resistance. Although this is an accurate approximation for a shot put travelling at 10 ms^{-1}, it's absolutely useless when considering a golf ball travelling at 100 ms^{-1}. Fortunately, the mathematical theory of air resistance is a bit too complicated for AS level so you probably won't have any difficult problems to solve. However, you will need to describe the effect of air resistance, especially the concept of terminal velocity.

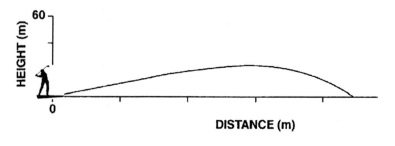

For a demonstration of air resistance you've probably put your hand outside the window of a moving car. The backward force on your hand is unmistakable. What causes this? The easiest way to explain it is that the air molecules are colliding with your hand and this leads to the backward force. The greater the velocity, the harder and more frequent the molecules collide with your hand so the air resistance force increases (in fact because of the harder collisions and the fact that they occur more frequently, the air resistance force is proportional to velocity squared).

Terminal velocity

This term is usually associated with parachutists and the standard question is, 'Explain why a falling sky diver will eventually reach terminal velocity.' [4]

air resistance

weight

Your answer should be similar to:

- The parachutist initially accelerates downward (with accel = 9.81 m s^{-2}).
- Air resistance increases as velocity increases.
- Eventually air resistance is equal and opposite to the weight.
- Zero resultant force so no acceleration (i.e. terminal velocity).

Another typical question would be: 'Explain why the terminal velocity of the parachutist is smaller after the parachute is opened.' [2]

Answer

- Parachute has a larger cross-sectional area.
- So that weight = air resistance at a lower velocity.

The graph shown is of a sky diver who reaches terminal velocity then opens the parachute.

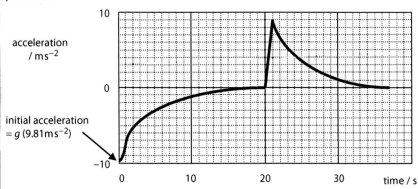

acceleration / m s^{-2}

initial acceleration = g (9.81 m s^{-2})

time / s

 quickpire

㉓ Explain why the initial acceleration of the parachutist dropping from rest is 9.81 m s^{-2}.

Grade boost

Short sentences or even bullet points are great for answers to 'explain' questions.

⊙≪≪≪quickfire

㉔ A car provides a constant driving force of 10 000 N and friction is a constant 500 N. Explain in terms of air resistance why the car will eventually reach a steady top speed (terminal velocity).

⊙≪≪≪quickfire

㉕ Air resistance is proportional to velocity squared. By what factor is air resistance increased when the velocity of a car increases from 20 miles per hour to 80 miles per hour?

(i) Explain why the acceleration changes direction and then decreases to zero. [5]

(ii) Explain why the area between the line and the x-axis must be overall negative. [2]

Answers

(i) When the parachute opens, the air resistance increases.

Now, air resistance is greater than the weight.

So resultant force and acceleration is upwards.

As the velocity decreases, air resistance decreases and the resultant upward force decreases.

Until air resistance = weight again and zero acceleration.

Note: The parachutist never travels upwards but the upward acceleration decreases the downward velocity – it is a deceleration in this case.

(ii) The total area between the x-axis and the line gives the velocity.

This velocity must be negative (downwards) QED.

In fact, the area for the first 20s will give the first terminal velocity (around -45 m s^{-1} if you want to work it out). The area for the next 17s is around 40 m s^{-1}. This means that the final terminal velocity will be -5 m s^{-1}.

Projectile motion

Now that you've studied a bit of air resistance theory, you have to forget it in order to do analysis on projectiles. The first statement in most projectile questions includes something like, 'Neglecting air resistance. . . .'

Typical projectile questions will involve cannon balls, arrows, shot puts or even flying fish but the underlying principle is this:

Vertical motion is completely independent of horizontal motion

What this means is that vertically we have a constant acceleration (9.81 m s^{-2}) but horizontally we have no acceleration, i.e. the horizontal velocity is always a constant. Don't forget this, this is essential – **the horizontal velocity is a constant**.

Although projectile motion may look new and complicated, you already have all the theory to answer any question that might be asked. All you have to do is apply the constant acceleration equations vertically and remember that the horizontal velocity is constant.

A difficult AS standard question

A shot putter launches the shot from a height of 1.99 m as shown.

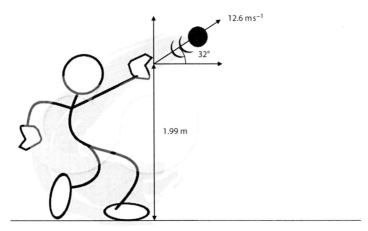

(i) Calculate the initial vertical and horizontal components of the velocity and sketch the trajectory of the shot put. [4]

(ii) Calculate the time taken for the shot put to reach its greatest height. [3]

(iii) Write down the time it takes for the shot put to return to its original height. [1]

(iv) Calculate the vertical velocity when the shot put strikes the ground. [3]

(v) Calculate the total time the shot put was in the air. [3]

(vi) Calculate the horizontal distance travelled by the shot put. [2]

Answers

(i) horizontal component $= 12.6 \times \cos 32 = 10.7 \text{ m s}^{-1}$ ✓

vertical component $= 12.6 \times \sin 32 = 6.7 \text{ m s}^{-1}$ ✓

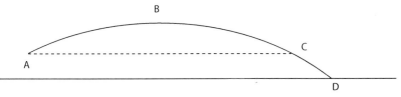

curve starting above ground and finishing at ground level ✓

curve shape reasonably accurate ✓

(ii) using $v = u + at \Rightarrow t = \dfrac{v - u}{a}$ ✓

$t = \dfrac{0 - 6.7}{-9.81} = 0.68 \text{s}$ ✓✓

$x =$	$u = 6.7$
$v = 0$	$a = -9.81$
$t = ?$	i.e from A to B on sketch

Pointer

Part of the reason why these questions are difficult is that they draw on previous vector work also.

Pointer

Look out for hidden information again. At the greatest height, the vertical velocity = 0.

Grade boost

You need to get all your signs correct. In this question, up is taken as positive throughout, so g = –9.81 m s^{-2}, downward velocities are negative and at the end the displacement is downwards so x = –1.99 m.

Grade boost

Make sure you know exactly which time interval you're using. In (ii) it was from A to B. In (iii), from B to C. In (iv), from A to D. In (v) from A to D.

Grade boost

Always make sure you use the correct values for u and v. There are so many values of different velocities that it's easy to get confused.

quickfire

㉖ Write down the values of u and v (the initial and final vertical velocities) for the following intervals:

(i) B to C

(ii) C to D

(iii) B to D

quickfire

㉗ Calculate the resultant velocity when the shot put strikes the ground (remember that velocity is a vector so you'll need the size of the velocity and an angle).

(iii) Another 0.68s (the path is symmetrical so that it will take the same time to come down) so total = 0.68 × 2 = 1.36s. ✓

(iv) There are many ways of doing this but this is probably the easiest.

$$v^2 = u^2 + 2ax$$ ✓

$$v^2 = 6.7^2 + 2(-9.81)(-1.99)$$ ✓

$$v^2 = 83.9$$

$x = -1.99$	$u = 6.7$
$v =$	$a = -9.81$
$t = ?$ i.e. from A to D on sketch	

$$v = \sqrt{83.9} = -9.2\,\mathrm{m\,s^{-1}} \text{ (because it's downward)}$$ ✓

(v) Again, there are many ways but it's best to avoid the equation with t^2 because this will give you a quadratic equation.

$$v = u + at \implies t = \frac{v-u}{a}$$ ✓

$$t = \frac{-9.2-6.7}{-9.81} = \frac{-15.9}{-9.81} = 1.62\,\mathrm{s}$$ ✓✓

$x = -1.99$	$u = 6.7$
$v = -9.2$	$a = -9.81$
$t = ?$ i.e. from A to D on sketch	

(vi) Remember, the **horizontal velocity is constant.**

horizontal distance = velocity × time ✓

= 10.7 × 1.62 = 17.3 m ✓

» Pointer

The way that the question is split up gives you the order to solve the problem – find the time first then get the horizontal velocity.

» Pointer

The other clue is 'time for the cannon ball to **drop**', i.e. the initial vertical velocity is zero.

» Pointer

This time down has been taken as positive so that $g = +9.81$ and v is positive.

Very difficult projectile question

A cannon shoots horizontally from atop a 42 m cliff and strikes a ship 320 m away. Calculate the initial velocity of the cannon ball (neglect air resistance). [4]

Describe briefly the effect of air resistance on the flight of the cannon ball. [3]

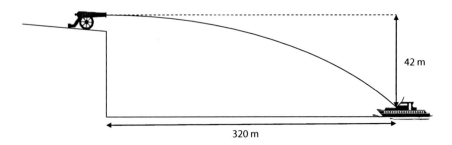

42 m

320 m

In truth, this question would normally be split into (i) calculate the time for the cannon ball to drop 42 m, (ii) calculate the initial velocity of the cannon ball. This gives you a couple of very important clues to solve the problem.

Answer

The ball is fired horizontally, so the initial vertical velocity is zero. Now you can use

$$x = ut + \frac{1}{2}at^2$$

$$42 = 0 + \frac{1}{2} \times 9.81t^2 \quad \checkmark$$

$x = 42$	$u = 0$
$v =$	$a = 9.81$
$t = ?$	

$$t^2 = \frac{2 \times 42}{9.81} = 8.56$$

$$t = \sqrt{8.56} = 2.9s \quad \checkmark$$

Remember that the horizontal velocity is a constant (v_h)

so   horizontal velocity = horizontal distance / time $\checkmark$

$v_h = 320 / 2.9 = 110 \ \mathrm{m\,s^{-1}}$ $\checkmark$

Air resistance always opposes the motion so:

- vertical velocity is always lower with air resistance $\checkmark$
- so time to fall must be longer $\checkmark$
- large resistive force horizontally due to high velocity $\checkmark$
- overall decrease in range due to larger effect horizontally $\checkmark$

(The mark scheme would probably say any 3 good points)

⊚≪≪≪ quickfire

㉘ A cricket ball trajectory is shown below

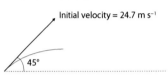

Initial velocity = 24.7 m s⁻¹

45°

(i) Calculate the initial vertical and horizontal velocities. [2]

(ii) Calculate the time the cricket ball takes to reach its greatest height. [2]

(iii) Calculate the greatest height the cricket ball reaches. [2]

(iv) Calculate the horizontal distance the cricket ball travels when it strikes the ground. [3]

quickfire

29 The train is pulled along a straight track at a constant velocity. How far has the train travelled before 1 MJ of work has been done?

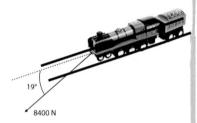

19°

8400 N

Energy concepts

Work

Work, like energy, is measured in Joules. Whenever work is mentioned, the following equation is the one to select from the WJEC data sheet:

$$W = Fx\cos\theta$$

where F is the force

and $x\cos\theta$ is the distance moved in the direction of the force.

This equation tells us the amount of useful energy that is used up by a force in pulling or pushing an object (the energy will be used up by whatever's supplying the force). Most often, but not always, the equation is simplified at A-level to

$$W = Fx$$

because the force is in the same direction as the movement.

Having defined work, you can get a better understanding of energy. You should be familiar with many types of energy: kinetic, potential, thermal, nuclear, etc. The standard definition of energy is the ability to do work. However, this definition becomes clearer when you realise that 200 J of kinetic energy could produce 200 J of work if 100% efficient. Likewise, 29 GJ of chemical energy in a tonne of coal could produce 29 GJ of work (if 100% efficient).

Typical example

A girl pulls a sled along flat snow for 0.9 km. Calculate the work done by the girl.

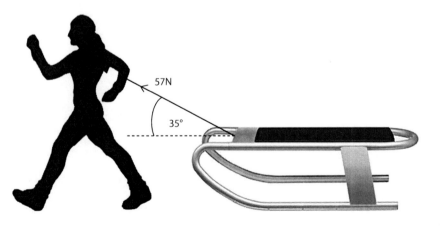

57N

35°

Answer

This is just a straightforward put the numbers into a formula question once you've converted the km to m (0.9 km = 900 m):

$$W = Fx\cos\theta = 57 \times 900 \times \cos 35° = 42 \text{ kJ}$$

Note that the work done is independent of how quickly the girl pulls the sled. The work done by the girl is 42 kJ whether she takes 10 minutes or 30 minutes to complete the journey.

However, if this work is done more quickly the power is higher because the power is the rate of energy transfer.

Example

The girl pulled the above sled 0.9 km in 10 minutes. Calculate the power.

$$P = \frac{\Delta W}{\Delta t} \quad \text{or} \quad \frac{W}{t} \text{ if you're not too happy with calculus}$$

$$= \frac{42000}{10 \times 60} = 70 \text{ W}$$

The definition of power can lead you to another important equation that does not appear on the WJEC data sheet. All you have to do is to combine the definition of work with the definition of power.

$$W = Fx\cos\theta$$

and $\quad P = \dfrac{W}{t} \quad$ so $\quad P = \dfrac{Fx\cos\theta}{t}$

but $\quad \dfrac{x}{t}$ is the velocity $P = Fv\cos\theta$

Although this is not exactly a proper proof of the equation

$$P = Fv\cos\theta$$

this is good enough to obtain full marks at this level. In fact, most of the time you'll be able to abbreviate the equation to

$$P = Fv$$

if the force is in the same direction as the velocity. These are very useful equations and give you the instantaneous power once you know the force and velocity (including their directions).

▲ Grade boost

Sometimes you can get wrong answers on your calculator if it's in the wrong mode. The angle in this question is in degrees so make sure your calculator is in DEG mode (and not in RAD mode which will be required in PH4).

◉ ‹‹‹‹ quickfire

(30) Venus orbits the Sun in a circular orbit. Explain why the work done by the gravitational force is zero.

Power = rate of energy transfer $\dfrac{\Delta W}{\Delta t}$ = (or the rate of work done).

Example

The rocket shown travels 3800 km in 12 minutes while the thrust remains a constant 160 000 N.

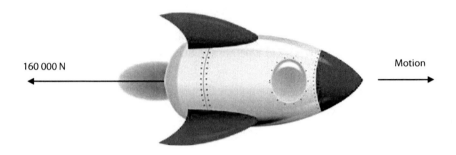

160 000 N
Motion

(i)   Calculate the work done.
(ii)   Calculate the mean power.

Answer

(i) $W = Fx\cos\theta = Fx = 160\ 000 \times 3800 \times 10^3 = 6.1 \times 10^{11}$ J

(ii) $P = \dfrac{W}{t} = \dfrac{6.1 \times 10^{11}}{12 \times 60} = 8.4 \times 10^8$ W

or $P = Fv = 6.1 \times 10^{11} \times \dfrac{3800 \times 10^3}{12 \times 60} = 8.4 \times 10^8$ W

Grade boost

More nasty unit tricks. Remember to convert minutes to seconds. 10 minutes = 10 × 60 s = 600 s and likewise with km and kW.

quickfire

㉛ The driving force produced by a Formula 1 car travelling at 95 m s⁻¹ is 7.4 kN. Calculate the power produced.

Example

The tension in a rope pulling a water skier is 870 N and the power provided to the water skier is 19 kW. The skier's velocity is in the same direction as the tension in the rope. Calculate the speed of the water skier.

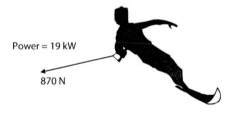

Power = 19 kW

870 N

Answer

$P = Fv \quad \Rightarrow \quad v = \dfrac{P}{F} = \dfrac{19\ 000}{870} = 22$ m s⁻¹

Force–distance graph

The only important thing that you need to remember regarding this type of graph is that the **area between the curve and the distance axis is the work done**.

By far the most common force–distance graph in this module is the force–extension graph for a spring:

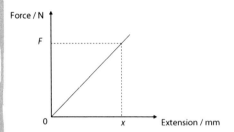

Note that the relationship between the force and the extension is:

    (i)   a straight line
    (ii)   passing through the origin.

This is Hooke's law – the force is directly proportional to the extension. The equation relating to Hooke's law is

$$F = kx$$

where k is called the spring constant or stiffness. Note that this equation does not appear in the WJEC data sheet – the syllabus states that you should recall this equation, so learn it! Anytime you'll see a question regarding a spring you'll need this equation.

Now, let's see what you can work out regarding the work done in stretching the above spring. All you have to do is work out the area between the line and the x-axis (i.e. the right angled triangle of sides x and F in the graph)

$$Area = W = \frac{1}{2} \times base \times height \times = \frac{1}{2} \times x \times F = \frac{1}{2}Fx$$

but $\qquad F = kx \quad \Rightarrow \quad W = \frac{1}{2}Fx = \frac{1}{2}(kx)x = \frac{1}{2}kx^2$

with a bit more algebra you also get $\qquad W = \frac{1}{2}\frac{F^2}{k}$

But what happens to this work that's done in extending the spring? The good news is that it's not lost; it becomes elastic potential energy in the spring. Finally you can write

$$Work\ done = energy\ stored\ by\ spring = \frac{1}{2}Fx = \frac{1}{2}kx^2 = \frac{1}{2}\frac{F^2}{k}$$

Unfortunately, it's only $W = \frac{1}{2}kx^2$ that you'll find on the WJEC data sheet. You'll

be expected to combine $W\frac{1}{2}kx^2$ with $F = kx$ to obtain the others.

Grade boost

Beware of this graph. It shows the length of the spring, not the extension so it doesn't go through the origin. You'll have to subtract the original length to get the extension – k is actually the gradient of the line.

Grade boost

Another nasty trick is to plot Force on the x-axis. Some pupils just calculate the gradient automatically and think that the answer is k. However, this time

$$k = \frac{1}{gradient}$$

Grade boost

You don't always have to convert cm to m. Here, it's easier to leave your answer in the unit $N\,cm^{-1}$. Unfortunately, this isn't always the case, so being able to convert from one unit to another is an essential skill for a physicist.

 Pointer

The derivations of $EPE = \frac{1}{2}Fx = \frac{1}{2}kx^2$ need to be learnt.

Calculate the stiffness (spring constant) from the following graphs

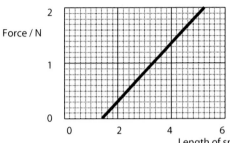

Answer
when force = 2.0 N
extension = 5.2 – 1.4 = 3.8 cm

$$k = \frac{F}{x} = \frac{2.0}{3.8} = 0.53\ N\,cm^{-1}$$

or $k = \frac{F}{x} = \frac{2.0}{0.038} = 53\ N\,m^{-1}$

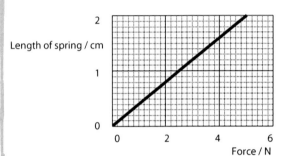

Answer
when force = 5.0 N
extension = 2.0 cm

$$k = \frac{F}{x} = \frac{5.0}{2.0} = 2.5\ N\,cm^{-1}$$

or $k = \frac{F}{x} = \frac{4.0}{0.016} = 250\ N\,m^{-1}$

Example

A spring of stiffness 38 $N\,m^{-1}$ is extended 2.8 cm using a mass suspended at one end of the spring. Calculate the mass and calculate the energy stored by the spring.

Answer

As ever with springs, you start from Hooke's law

$$F = kx$$

and remember that the force is the weight of the mass (mg). So

$$mg = kx \quad \Rightarrow \quad m = \frac{kx}{g} = \frac{38 \times 0.028}{9.81} = 0.11\ kg$$

The energy stored is just a case of choosing the right equation and putting numbers in:

$$energy\ stored = \frac{1}{2}kx^2 = \frac{1}{2}38 \times 0.028^2 = 0.015\ J$$

Nasty question

In the last example, before the spring reached a steady extension of 2.8 cm, the mass was attached to the unextended spring and allowed to drop. Compare the work done by the gravitational force with the energy stored by the spring and try to account for any difference.

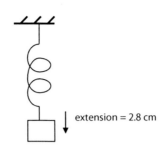

extension = 2.8 cm

Answer

You already know that the final energy stored by the spring is 0.015 J. What about the work done by the gravitational force?

$$W = Fx\cos\theta = Fx = mg \times x = 0.11 \times 9.81 \times 0.028 = 0.030 \text{ J}$$

but this is twice as much as the energy stored by the spring, so what's happened to the other 0.015 J?

The answer is simpler than you might think. The first time the mass dropped to an extension of 2.8 cm it had 0.015 J of elastic potential energy but it was also moving. In fact, it was moving at its highest speed and so had kinetic energy. How much kinetic energy is obvious – it accounts for the missing 0.015 J of energy.

However, that's not the end of the story because eventually the kinetic energy dies away and the mass ends up stationary with an extension of 2.8 cm. The reason for this is that air resistance is continually slowing down the motion of the mass until the mass stops moving. This energy eventually ends up as kinetic energy of the gas particles in the air through collisions with the mass. This means that the thermal (or internal) energy of the gas particles eventually increases by 0.015 J (which is tiny as thermal energy goes!).

This last discussion brings you quite nicely to the next important energy topic.

quickfire

㉞ How much kinetic energy does a 20 tonne lorry travelling at 30 m s⁻¹ have?
(1 tonne = 1000 kg)

quickfire

㉟ Calculate the mass of an object travelling at 370 m s⁻¹ with a kinetic energy of 3.2×10^{-21} J.

quickfire

㊱ At what speed does a peregrine falcon of mass 0.69 kg travel when it has 2.9 kJ of kinetic energy?

The principle of conservation of energy

This principle comes up regularly (on all papers not just PH1) and usually involves you having to explain where the missing energy has gone (see the last example). Sometimes, the examiner will ask you to state the principle first before going on later to play 'find the missing energy' – in which case you just quote something similar to the definition in the key term.

What this principle means, essentially, is that energy is never actually lost or gained but that it gets transferred from one type of energy to another (e.g. a falling brick – gravitational potential energy to kinetic energy).

Kinetic energy

You've known for many years that kinetic energy is the energy possessed by moving objects and you should remember from GCSE that

$$\textit{Kinetic Energy}\ (\mathrm{KE}) = \frac{1}{2}mv^2$$

In any case, you'll find the equation $E = \frac{1}{2}mv^2$ on the WJEC data sheet.

Work–energy relationship

If you combine kinetic energy, work and the principle of conservation of energy you can obtain a very interesting result.

Consider a lorry accelerating from an initial speed u to a final speed v. The change in kinetic energy will be

$$\textit{change in KE} = \frac{1}{2}mv^2 - \frac{1}{2}mu^2$$

But what provides this increase in kinetic energy? It must be the driving force (provided by the engine via the wheels, etc.). But you can calculate the work done by this driving force.

$$W = Fx$$

The work done will be the driving force times the distance moved in the direction of the force. All you have to do now is apply conservation of energy:

$$\text{work done} = \text{change in KE}$$

$$Fx = \frac{1}{2}mv^2 - \frac{1}{2}mu^2$$

This equation is known as the work–energy relationship and it's on the WJEC data sheet. This equation usually provides a difficult 4 marks somewhere on the long mechanics question on the PH1 paper.

quickfire

㊲ At what speed is a helium atom travelling if it has a kinetic energy of 8.3×10^{-22} J?

(Mass of a He atom = 6.6×10^{-27} kg.)

quickfire

㊳ A toy car accelerates from 1.2 m s^{-1} to 5.5 m s^{-1} using a constant driving force of 0.85 N over a distance of 13.2 cm. Calculate the mass of the toy car.

[Hint: factorise the m in the equation i.e. $Fx = \frac{1}{2}m\left(v^2 - u^2\right)$.]

Example

A cyclist of total mass 92 kg stops cycling and slows down from 18 m s^{-1} to 13 m s^{-1} in a distance of 47 m. Calculate the mean resistive force acting on the cyclist.

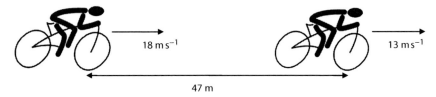

18 m s^{-1} 13 m s^{-1}

47 m

Answer

$$Fx = \frac{1}{2}mv^2 - \frac{1}{2}mu^2$$

$$F = \frac{\frac{1}{2}mv^2 - \frac{1}{2}mu^2}{x}$$

$$F = \frac{\frac{1}{2}90 \times 18^2 - \frac{1}{2}90 \times 13^2}{48} = 150\,\text{N}$$

Gravitational potential energy (GPE)

In some way, you've already derived an equation for the GPE when you considered the work done by the gravitational force for the mass on the spring earlier. Now, consider a more general case. A mass m is lifted a height Δh:

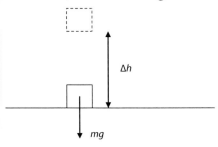

Δh

mg

The force required to lift the mass is mg and the mass is lifted a distance Δh in the same direction as the force (or in the opposite direction to its weight).

All you have to do now is apply the definition of work and the conservation of energy.

work done = $Fx = mg\Delta h$

work done = increase in gravitational potential energy = $mg\Delta h$

One thing to note here is that you need to lift the weight with a force of exactly mg and not a force greater than mg. If you lifted the mass with a force greater than mg, the mass would accelerate and gain kinetic energy also.

Example

What height does a 55 kg lady need to gain in order to increase her GPE by 1900 J?

Answer

$$mg\Delta h = 1900 \quad \Rightarrow \quad \Delta h = \frac{1900}{mg} = \frac{1900}{55 \times 9.81} = 3.5\,\text{m}$$

Example

On the Moon, a mass of 3.60 kg raised 2.20 m above the surface of the Moon has a GPE of 12.9 J. Calculate the acceleration due to gravity on the Moon.

Answer

$$mg\Delta h = 12.9 \quad \Rightarrow \quad g = \frac{12.9}{m\Delta h} = \frac{12.9}{3.60 \times 2.20} = 1.63\,\text{m s}^{-2}$$

Efficiency

This is the final topic in the energy concepts and you should already be reasonably familiar with efficiency from GCSE. Efficiency is quoted as a percentage and can be seen on the WJEC data sheet.

$$\text{Efficiency} = \frac{\text{Useful energy obtained}}{\text{Energy input}} \times 100\%$$

quickfire

㊴ A 44 tonne lorry brakes from 25.5 m s^{-1} to rest in a distance of 58.8 m.

(i) Calculate the initial KE of the lorry. [2]

(ii) Write down the work done on the brakes. [1]

(iii) Calculate the mean braking force. [2]

(iv) Explain this process in terms of conservation of energy. [3]

(v) Explain why the efficiency of this braking process is 0%. [1]

Example

A tennis ball of mass 0.0575 kg is dropped from a height of 25.9 m. When the ball strikes the ground it has a speed of 22.1 m s^{-1}. Calculate the efficiency of the conversion of GPE into KE and explain what happens to the missing energy.

Answer

$$GPE = mgh = 0.0575 \times 9.81 \times 25.9 = 14.61\,\text{J}$$

$$KE = \frac{1}{2}mv^2 = \frac{1}{2} \times 0.0575 \times 22.1^2 = 14.04\,\text{J}$$

$$\text{Efficiency} = \frac{\text{Useful energy obtained}}{\text{Energy input}} \times 100\% = \frac{14.04}{14.61} \times 100\% = 96\%$$

The 0.57 J of energy that is lost (i.e. 14.61 – 14.04) is lost to the gas particles of the air and will end up as random kinetic energy of the gas particles.

You are expected to know a little about the forces that cause a reduction in efficiency. These forces are often called resistive forces or frictional forces but sometimes are referred to as dissipative forces. They are dissipative forces because they are associated with 'wasted' energy.

The two most important examples of dissipative forces are:

1. Friction

   - Frictional forces inside a wheel bearing as it rotates. This would provide an overall resistive force on the motion of the wheel. The friction would cause an increase in temperature of the bearings – an increased internal energy of the bearings.

   - Friction between a skier's ski and the snow. Again, this force resists the motion of the skier and the friction causes an increase in the temperature of the ski and the snow, i.e. increased internal energy of the ski and the snow.

2. Air/water resistance

   At this level you don't need to know any more than has been stated previously. An object moving through a gas or a liquid will transfer some of its kinetic energy to the particles in the gas/liquid. This will end up as a slight increase in the random kinetic energy of the particles of the gas/liquid which is an increase in internal energy of the gas/liquid.

quickfire

40 A skier of mass 83 kg accelerates from 18.3 m s^{-1} to 27.8 m s^{-1} over a distance of 54.7 m.

   (i) Calculate the change in KE of the skier. [2]

   (ii) Calculate the mean resultant force acting on the skier. [2]

   (iii) The GPE lost by the skier in this process was 22 500 J. Calculate the mean frictional force. [3]

quickfire

41 Explain in terms of forces and energy why a submarine providing 9500 N of thrust will not keep accelerating indefinitely.

quickfire

42 Explain briefly what happens to the work done by the gravitational force when a sky diver is falling at his terminal velocity.

>> Pointer

All this charging and discharging is to do with the movement of electrons (we're not interested in movement of protons because they're stuck inside the nuclei of the fixed atoms).

Conduction of electricity

Electric charges

Before getting started with anything new, here are some very basic facts that you should already know:

- Protons (located in the nucleus of an atom) have a positive charge.
- Electrons (orbiting the nucleus) have a negative charge.
- Like charges attract, opposites repel.
- Electrical current is a flow of charge.
- Conductors allow charge to flow through them.
- Insulators do not allow charge to flow through them.
- Insulators can be charged through rubbing.

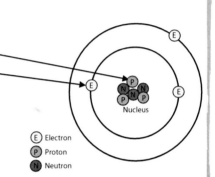

(E) Electron
(P) Proton
(N) Neutron

Historically, Benjamin Franklin decided to call the charge given to a glass rod rubbed with silk the name 'positive' and the charge on an amber rod rubbed with fur was called 'negative'. As a result of this arbitrary decision by Franklin, you have negatively charged electrons going the 'wrong' way around most electrical circuits.

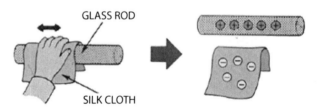

GLASS ROD

SILK CLOTH

What happens when a glass rod is rubbed with a silk cloth?

The friction itself is not essential – this just ensures that the two materials are brought very close together so that the electrons can move to the material that they prefer (remember, in chemistry, some atoms with nearly full outer shells are particularly 'fond' of electrons). In this case, the electrons leave the glass rod and move onto the silk cloth. The glass rod will be positive but the silk cloth will also be negative by the same number of electrons (since no electrons were created or destroyed in this process).

There aren't many types of question that can be asked regarding static electricity but here's a couple of examples to give you the idea of the level of understanding required.

Example

Explain why a student holding a metal rod cannot charge the metal rod using a silk cloth.

Answer

The metal rod will not hold a charge because it is a conductor. Imagine if the metal rod were negative then electrons would be able to flow through the rod and into the student's hand. If the conductor were positive, electrons would flow from the student and into the rod (but remember, this isn't the case for an insulator).

Example

An amber rod is rubbed with fur. The amber rod then touches a metal rod suspended from a thin plastic insulating wire. Explain why the metal rod is negatively charged when the amber rod is removed.

Answer

As the amber rod is rubbed with the fur, electrons move from the fur to the amber and the amber becomes negatively charged (and the fur positive).

When this negatively charged amber rod touches the metal rod, electrons close to the metal can move onto the metal rod. These electrons cannot move away from the metal rod because it is insulated due to the plastic wire.

When the amber rod is removed, the extra electrons remain on the metal rod and the rod remains negatively charged

Grade boost

All these types of questions will require explanations so keep your sentences short and to the point.

» Pointer

The conductor can hold a charge in this case because it's insulated due to the plastic wire.

quickfire

43 A cellulose acetate rod is rubbed by a duster and becomes positively charged. Explain this process briefly in terms of electrons and explain how much charge is held by the duster.

quickfire

44 A positively charged cellulose acetate rod picks up small pieces of paper which are neutral. Explain the process briefly in terms of electrons.

quickfire

45 Explain why a metal sphere when charged holds the charge on the outer surface of the sphere.

The most difficult question that an examiner could ask regarding these types of static electricity charges would be an explanation of charging by induction and the resulting attractive force. Although this is not explicitly stated in the syllabus, all the theory relating to it is and so the examiner could ask about it if they were feeling particularly evil. In any case, if you can understand charging by induction, you'll be well on your way to obtaining good marks in this subject.

When a charged object is brought near a neutral object there is always an attractive force between the two objects. The explanation for the force is simple once you approach the explanation from the point of view of electrons.

As an example, you should have been shown sometime a balloon being charged (by rubbing with non-greasy hair). When this balloon is placed against a wall it stays there (there's an attractive force holding it to the wall).

First, the friction causes the balloon to become negatively charged (and the non-greasy hair to be positive).

When the balloon is brought near the wall, the electrons in the wall will be repelled by the negative charge on the balloon. Leaving the wall near the balloon positively charged.

You'll notice now that, although the wall is still neutral, the positive charges are closer to the balloon than the negative charges. This means that there's an overall attractive force between the balloon and the wall.

This is what is meant by charging by induction – the negative charge on the balloon repels the electrons so that you get a separation of the charges in the wall. This separation of charges always leads to an attractive force. In some respects the term charging by induction is confusing because the wall does not get charged up, it still remains neutral – it's the movement of electrons that causes a separation of the charges.

Measuring charge

Charge is measured in units of coulomb and can be measured with a device called a coulomb meter. Some coulomb meters measure static charge (see diagram) while others sit in a circuit like an ammeter and tell you the total amount of charge that has passed through.

The coulomb is rather a large unit of charge and you get some idea of this when you know that the charge on an electron is -1.60×10^{-19} C.

⊙》》》》quickfire

⑯ How many electrons are there in a coulomb of charge?

Question

A glass rod holds a charge of 25.0 nC. How many electrons has it lost?

Answer

$$\text{Number of electrons} = \frac{25.0 \times 10^{-9}}{1.60 \times 10^{-19}} = 1.56 \times 10^{10}$$

Current and charge

You already know that current is a flow of charge but you might not have come across the more precise definition. Current is the rate of flow of charge. This appears as an equation on the WJEC data sheet:

$I = \dfrac{\Delta Q}{\Delta t}$ but you can usually write $I = \dfrac{Q}{t}$

This equation means that if you look at any point in a circuit and a charge Q passes that point in time t, then the current is $I = \dfrac{Q}{t}$

As you know, the unit of current is the ampere (A) but from the equation above you'll see straight away that A = C s^{-1} (i.e. a current of one amp is equal to 1 coulomb of charge passing per second).

Grade boost

It's surprising how often you have to multiply or divide by 1.60×10^{-19} (the size of e, in coulomb) to obtain an answer in A-level physics. The only problem is deciding whether or not to divide or multiply. If in doubt do both – one of the answers will be OK and the other will be completely stupid!

⊙》》》》quickfire

⑰ The total amount of charge that passed through a circuit was 18.6 C and the current was a constant 450 mA. For how much time was the current flowing?

Question

If 25 C of charge passes through a point in a circuit in 1 minute. What is the current?

Answer

$I = \dfrac{\Delta Q}{\Delta t} = \dfrac{25}{60} = 0.40 \ A$ (note the conversion 1 minute = 60 s)

Drift velocity = the small average speed of electrons in a conductor due to an applied pd.

n = the number of *free* electrons per cubic metre.

>> *Pointer*

This LED question is nastier because it's a two-step question. You need to be thinking ahead, e.g. I can get the charge from current and time then I can get the number of electrons by dividing by 1.60×10^{-19} C.

quickfire

(48) The total number of electrons that passed through a circuit in 1 hour was 7.87×10^{23}. Calculate the mean current.

>> *Pointer*

Remember this theory of free electrons in metals, it'll come up again in explanations of resistance increasing with temperature.

Grade boost

Just remember the diagram and the four steps. This proof comes up once every two or three PH1 papers and when it does it's worth around 5 marks – that's almost a whole grade!

Nastier question

The current in a LED is 35.2 mA. How many electrons have flowed through it in 1 hour?

Answer

$$I = \frac{\Delta Q}{\Delta t} \quad \Rightarrow \quad \Delta Q = I \times \Delta t = 35.2 \times 10^{-3} \times 60 \times 60 = 127 \text{ C}$$

$$\text{Number of electrons} = \frac{127}{1.60 \times 10^{-19}} = 7.9 \times 10^{20}$$

Now that you know the relationship between charge and current you're almost ready for possibly the trickiest bit of theory on the whole syllabus that you must be able to derive yourself. But first, let's check that you understand how electric currents arise in a metal.

In this next theory, you only need to consider the free electrons of the metal (most of the electrons in metals are not free but you don't need to consider those). It's the free electrons that can move around and contribute towards an electrical current. The motion of the free electrons is random and similar to the motion of gas particles, i.e. they move about quickly then have collisions. Because of this, sometimes the free electrons in a metal are called a 'free electron gas'. Electrons usually travel about 40 nm at a speed of around 2×10^6 m s^{-1} in between collisions, which means that their time in between collisions is about 20 fs. However, you have to remember that before a potential difference (pd or voltage) is applied, the mean velocity of these electrons is exactly zero – their motion is completely random in all directions so the vector average of velocity is zero. As soon as a pd is applied these electrons will be accelerated by the pd in between collisions and they'll end up with a tiny little average speed that will constitute a current.

Consider the following cross-section of a wire where we have a lot of electrons all moving to the right with a **drift velocity** v.

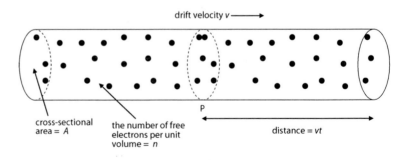

drift velocity $v \longrightarrow$

P

cross-sectional area = A

the number of free electrons per unit volume = n

distance = vt

Each of those dots is meant to represent a free electron (there'd be a lot more free electrons in a real metal unless it's a **very** thin wire). In order to calculate the current you need to know the charge passing a certain point every second – let's look at point P. You need to consider some interval of time t. In this time, the electrons have moved on a distance vt. So, if you can count all the electrons in the tube to the right of point P you're on your way to calculating the current.

These are the four essential steps:

1. Volume (right of P) = $vt \times A$ (volume = length × area for the cylinder)
2. Number of electrons = $vtA \times n$ (number = volume × n)
3. Charge = $vtAn \times e$ (charge = number × charge of electron)
4. Current (I) = $\dfrac{vtAne}{t} = nAve$ (current = charge / time)

i.e. $I = nAve$ QED

Remember: you need no more than a clear diagram and the four steps above (you don't need an introduction paragraph and the clarification in the brackets).

Now that you've derived the equation let's get some idea of the type of values that can come up.

Example

In copper there are 8.5×10^{28} free electrons per cubic metre ($n = 8.5 \times 10^{28}$ m^{-3}). A copper wire of diameter 0.213 mm carries a current of 0.35A. Calculate the drift velocity of the electrons.

Answer

This is a two-step calculation but it should be reasonably obvious that you can get A (the cross-sectional area) from the diameter.

$$A = \pi r^2 = \pi\left(\frac{d}{2}\right)^2 = \pi\frac{d^2}{4} = \pi \times \frac{(0.213 \times 10^{-3})^2}{4} = 35.6 \times 10^{-9} \text{ m}^2$$

then using

$$I = nAve \implies v = \frac{I}{nAe} = \frac{0.35}{8.5 \times 10^{28} \times 35.6 \times 10^{-9} \times 1.60 \times 10^{-19}} = 7.2 \times 10^{-4} \text{ m s}^{-1}$$

There are two important things to remember about the figures here:

1. n, the number of free electrons per m³ is a very large number for metals, around 10^{28} free electrons per m³.
2. v, the drift velocity is a small number for metals, less than a mm per second even for this thin wire.

Grade boost

Often you'll have to convert a diameter into a cross-sectional area, especially when you're using $I = nAve$. It's worth remembering

$$A = \pi\frac{d^2}{4}.$$

Grade boost

Sometimes you are asked to state the meaning of n. A common answer is that it's the number of electrons per m³ – wrong. You need to say that n is the number of *free* electrons per m³.

⊙《《《 quickfire

49 The current in a tungsten wire is 1.20 A and the drift velocity of electrons is 2.35 mm s^{-1}. The number of free electrons per m³ in tungsten is 6.3×10^{28} m^{-3}. Use the table to find the gauge of the wire.

Standard wire gauge	Diameter/ mm
31	0.295
32	0.274
33	0.254
34	0.234
35	0.213
36	0.193
37	0.173
38	0.152

≫ Pointer

In order to provide the same current, electrons have to move faster in a thinner wire. This is worth remembering.

Potential difference (pd) between two points = the energy converted from electrical potential energy to some other form per coulomb of charge flowing from one point to the other. Unit = JC^{-1}.

The resistance of a conductor = the pd (V) placed across it divided by the resulting current (I) through it. $R = V/I$ Unit: ohm (Ω) [$= VA^{-1}$].

Ohm's law = the current flowing through a metal wire at constant temperature is proportional to the pd across it.

Resistance

Potential difference (pd)

The actual definition of **pd** you can see in the key term and this comes up regularly on PH1 papers. The definition itself might not make all that much sense to you and this is where the penguins come to the rescue.

If you look at the toy to the left you'll see that it works through having a mechanised elevator lift the penguins to the top, the penguins then slide to the bottom where they get picked up again by the elevator. This is very similar to the way charges flow around a circuit. The elevator is similar to a cell; it provides the gravitational potential energy (GPE) to the penguins who then gradually lose all this GPE until they arrive back at the elevator which provides the GPE again. In an electrical circuit, the cell provides electrical potential energy (EPE) to the charges which then lose this EPE gradually until they arrive back at the cell where they once more gain EPE.

The reason why this comparison explains that pd is associated with energy per unit charge is this:

- If the elevator were empty it wouldn't be doing any work (the elevator is extremely light and frictionless!).
- The more penguins that are on the elevator, the more work is done by the elevator. In fact, the work done by the elevator is proportional to the number of penguins that have been lifted by it.

In the same way, the work done by a cell in a circuit is proportional to the amount of charge that has flowed through it. The work done (W) by a cell of emf (V) when a charge (Q) has flowed is:

$W = QV$ which rearranged gives $V = \dfrac{W}{Q}$ which is the definition of pd applied to the whole circuit.

Ohm's law

The resistance of a conductor is defined by the equation:

$$R = \frac{V}{I}$$

This tells you that the unit, the ohm, (Ω) is the same as VA^{-1}. See the statement of Ohm's law in the key terms. 'State Ohm's law' is a favourite question on PH1 so you need to learn it.

The equation can be rearranged to $I = \dfrac{V}{R}$ and you should see that V and I are directly proportional (as long as R remains constant, which it does as long as the temperature remains constant). Here's the standard Ohm's law graph. Note that the voltage appears on the x-axis so that the gradient will be $\dfrac{1}{R}$.

This graph is a current–voltage graph and is often abbreviated to 'I–V graph'.

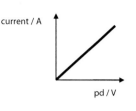

Example

1 The pd across a resistor is 3.2 V and the current is 0.18 A. Calculate its resistance.

2 When a charge of 76 mC flows in a resistor the energy dissipated is 58 J.
   (i) Calculate the pd across the resistor
   (ii) Calculate the current, given that the charge flowed in 3.5 s
   (iii) Calculate the resistance of the resistor.

Answers

1 $R = \dfrac{V}{I} = \dfrac{3.2}{0.18} = 18\ \Omega$

2 (i) $V = \dfrac{W}{Q} = \dfrac{58}{0.076} = 760\ V$

   (ii) $I = \dfrac{Q}{t} = \dfrac{0.076}{3.5} = 0.022\ A \quad (= 22\ mA)$

   (iii) $R = \dfrac{V}{I} = \dfrac{760}{0.022} = 35000\ \Omega \quad (= 35\ k\Omega)$

Electrical power

If you combine the definition of pd with the definition of power and current you can derive a very useful equation for electrical power.

First, you start with the work done $\qquad\qquad W = QV$

then divide this equation by the time $\qquad \dfrac{W}{t} = \dfrac{QV}{t}$

but $\quad \dfrac{W}{t}$ = power (P) and $\dfrac{Q}{t}$ = current (I), $\quad P = IV$

but since $V = IR \qquad P = IV = I \times IR = I^2R \quad$ or $\quad P = IV = \dfrac{V}{R} \times V = \dfrac{V^2}{R}$

These are three useful ways of calculating power, but only $P = IV$ appears on the WJEC data sheet.

quickfire

50 Calculate the amount of energy transferred when a charge of 28 C flows through a pd of 12 V.

quickfire

51 The current in a 82 Ω resistor is 72 mA. Calculate:
   (i) The pd across the resistor.
   (ii) The charge that flows in 1 minute 20 s.
   (iii) The energy dissipated in the resistor.

quickfire

52 Calculate the power dissipated in a 36 Ω resistor with a current of 0.45 A in it.

quickfire

53 A mains (230 V) electrical kettle dissipates a power of 3.0 kW. Calculate the current.

quickfire

54 A mains (230 V) electric fire has a resistance of 55 Ω. Calculate its power.

I–V graphs that you need to learn

Metallic conductor at a constant temperature

The graph is a straight line through the origin (signifying $I \propto V$). Often, on an I–V graph, you plot the negative values also, this is because not all electrical devices behave the same when the voltage is reversed (see the diode graph).

This brings us rather conveniently to the next I–V graph that you need to know – the diode.

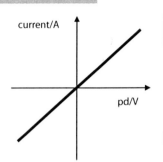

Diode

When the diode is connected the 'correct' way (forward biased), it starts to conduct properly when the applied pd is around 0.7 V (this is standard for a silicon diode). When the diode is connected the 'wrong' way (reverse biased) the diode does not conduct electricity. The I–V graph for a light emitting diode (LED) is exactly the same except that these won't start conducting properly (for forward bias) until the pd reaches around 2–3 V (this is also when they start giving off plenty of light).

This is the only information you need regarding the diode – just remember the shape of the graph and only allowing current in one direction (you don't need to know the values of 0.7 V for a silicon diode or 3 V for an LED).

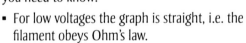

>> *Pointer*

Never allow the gradient of a filament of a light bulb I–V graph to reach zero (flat) because the current must always increase as the pd increases. Also, never allow the line of the I–V graph for a diode to become vertical – this is not physically possible (except for a superconductor – see later).

Filament of a lamp

There are two important parts to this graph that you need to know:

- For low voltages the graph is straight, i.e. the filament obeys Ohm's law.
- The gradient decreases for higher voltages. This is because the resistance is increasing.

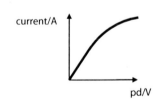

Why does the resistance increase? Because the temperature of the filament is increasing. At its full rating the filament usually operates at 2500°C.

Now it's time to return to the 'free electron gas' (see the previous section on conduction page 48) theory in order to explain why a metal's resistance increases with temperature. There are two important things that happen as the temperature rises. First, the electrons travel faster in between collisions. Second, ions in the metal lattice vibrate more.

Both these effects decrease the time in between collisions. If the collisions occur more frequently, then the electrons will have a smaller drift velocity because they can't be accelerated to the same speed in between collisions. This leads to a decreased current and therefore a higher resistance.

Investigating the variation of a wire's resistance with temperature

This is the standard school laboratory method:

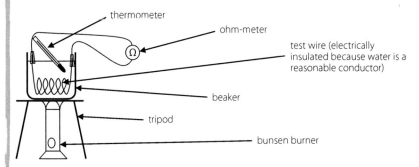

- Heat the water to boiling point.
- Take readings of the resistance every 10°C from 20°C up to 100°C.
- Added detail: stir the water for uniform temperature, subtract the zero error from the resistance values (see PH3 notes and next experiment).

This is one of two experiments that you need to know how to describe, so learn it. You should also know that the results give a linear variation of resistance with respect to temperature over a wide range of temperature.

Resistivity

Whereas resistance is a property of a particular resistor, resistivity is a property of a material. For a given metal, the resistivity is a constant regardless of the shape of the metal sample. The following equation defines the resistivity:

$$R = \frac{\rho l}{A}$$

R = resistance of the sample (usually a wire or cylinder)
l = length (of the wire or cylinder)
A = cross-sectional area (of the wire or cylinder)
ρ = resistivity of the material (usually a metal)

Let's rearrange the equation to make ρ the subject $\rho = \dfrac{RA}{l}$. Then we'll put in units to obtain the unit of resistivity:

$$[\rho] = \frac{\Omega m^2}{m} = \Omega m$$

so the unit of resistivity is $\Omega\,m$.

Now for the second experiment whose description you have to learn.

quickfire

⑤⑤ Explain why the resistance of a metal wire increases with temperature.

Measuring the resistivity of a metal wire (nichrome in this case)

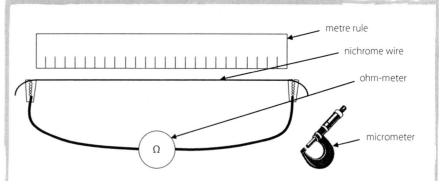

Method

1. Use a micrometer to measure the diameter of the wire. Do this in various places and take the mean, allowing for zero error [see PH3].
2. Use the ohm-meter to take a measurement of the resistance for 1.000 m of the nichrome wire (any reasonable length would be ok), allowing for zero error [see PH3]. The length should be measured between the crocodile clips.

Results

Length of nichrome wire = 1.000 m, 1.000 m (taken twice as a check)

Zero error of micrometer = 0.00 mm, 0.00 mm (taken twice as a check)

Zero error of ohm-meter = 0.4 Ω, 0.4 Ω (taken twice as a check)

Thickness readings for nichrome wire = 0.25 mm, 0.26 mm, 0.26 mm, 0.25 mm

mean = 0.255 mm

Resistance reading for 1.000 m of nichrome wire = 21.6 Ω, 21.6 Ω (taken twice as a check)

Conclusions

The value of resistivity obtained for nichrome was 1.08×10^{-6} Ω m with an estimated uncertainty of 8%. This is in excellent agreement with published values for nichrome (e.g. http://www.kayelaby.npl.co.uk).

There's more detail in the above experiment than you need but these are the details that you must remember:

1. The apparatus and how to measure resistance, length and thickness of the wire.
2. How to measure the resistivity from your data (see Quickfire 56 and 58).

quickfire

⑤⑥ Use the data in the experiment to confirm that the area of the wire is 51.1 $\times 10^{-9}$ m^{-2} and that the resistivity of the wire is 1.08×10^{-6} Ω m.

quickfire

⑤⑦ A block of the alloy constantan has dimensions 0.3 cm × 0.3 cm × 250.0 cm and its resistance when measured along its longest side is 0.136 Ω. Calculate the resistivity of constantan.

quickfire

⑤⑧ In an experiment to measure the resistivity of a metal, the resistance of a wire is measured as the length is varied. A graph is then plotted of resistance against length. How would you obtain the resistivity using the gradient of the graph?

Superconductivity

On 8 April 1911, the Dutch physicist Heike Kamerlingh Onnes found that the resistance of a solid mercury wire at 4.2K (−269°C) suddenly dropped to zero. This was an incredible discovery that started a whole new research area into **superconductors** and Heike Kamerlingh Onnes was later rewarded with a Nobel Prize.

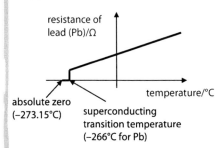

resistance of lead (Pb)/Ω

temperature/°C

absolute zero (−273.15°C)

superconducting transition temperature (−266°C for Pb)

Many but not all metals are superconductors at temperatures close to absolute zero (i.e. at temperatures of a few kelvin or around −270°C). Some examples of superconductors are aluminium, tin, lead and mercury. Their resistance drops suddenly to zero at a special temperature called the **superconducting transition temperature**.

It's particularly interesting to note that one of the metals that does **not** become a superconductor at temperatures close to absolute zero is copper. However, in 1986, it was discovered that some copper-based ceramics became superconductors at 'high' temperatures. This caused another new explosion into superconductor research and the race for the first room temperature superconductor continues. In 1987, the 'high' temperature superconductors had reached liquid nitrogen temperatures (77 K or −196°C) and in 2011, a century after the initial discovery in 1911, the world record is around 160 K (or −110°C).

Perhaps, superconductors seem like interesting theoretical devices that have no use in the real world because of the low temperatures required. This is not the case, superconductors are used daily in hospitals, particle accelerators and even on the record breaking Maglev train in Japan. In all these applications, superconductors are used to obtain very large magnetic fields because they are able to carry huge currents without heating (no resistance means no heating). In part, this is made possible because liquid nitrogen is only a few pence per litre and liquid helium is about a few pounds per litre.

Applications

1   Magnetic resonance imagers (MRI scanners), used almost continually in hospitals. The superconductors provide the large magnetic fields.

2   Particle accelerators – the superconductors provide strong magnetic fields to bend the particle beams.

3   Maglev train – on-board levitating magnets use high temperature superconductors cooled by liquid nitrogen.

DC circuits

Conservation of charge

This can be applied to all circuits and essentially comes down to this – electrons are not created or destroyed in a circuit.

The most obvious use of conservation of charge is to get rid of the terrible misconception that some younger pupils have at GCSE level. In the circuit shown, $I_1 = I_2$ because electrons don't suddenly disappear (or multiply or build up) in the resistor. If 2 million free electrons enter the resistor then 2 million free electrons exit the resistor and it must be that the two currents are equal. This theory can be extended to parallel circuits.

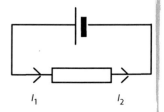

If you look at junction A where current I_1 splits into I_2 and I_3, you can apply conservation of charge to the junction. You can't lose or gain any charges (electrons) at the junction (either A or B) and the result of this is:

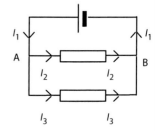

$$I_1 = I_2 + I_3$$

Another way of expressing this conservation of charge is – 'the sum of the current going into a junction is equal to the sum of the current leaving a junction'.

Example

Apply conservation of charge to the following junction:

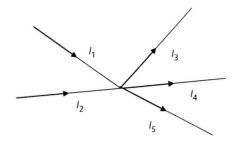

Answer

The current going in is $I_1 + I_2$ and the current going out is $I_3 + I_4 + I_5$, hence,

$$I_1 + I_2 = I_3 + I_4 + I_5$$

Conservation of energy

You can also apply conservation of energy to circuits. For instance, in the circuit on the right you use the definition of pd and apply it to the circuit as a whole. The pd supplied by the cell is 3 V. Using $V = IR$, you can calculate the pd across both resistors. This will be $IR_1 + IR_2$. Since pd is

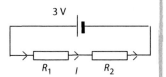

the energy per unit charge, you can consider one coulomb of charge and apply conservation of energy i.e. $3 = IR_1 + IR_2$.

This is true for any series circuit, if you add up all the pds across individual components you'll get the pd across the supply.

However, you can also apply conservation of energy to parallel circuits and obtain an equally important result. Consider an electron going through the top resistor and another electron going through the bottom resistor, they then meet up in B. You conclude that both these electrons must have exactly the same potential energy. This means that the pds across components in parallel are equal (this must always be true otherwise electrons taking different routes will have different potential energies).

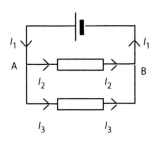

quickfire

59 Calculate the missing current

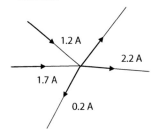

quickfire

60 Calculate the pd across each of the three resistors in the diagram and the pd supplied by the cell.

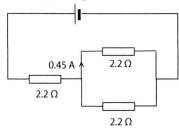

Combinations of resistances

In series

The combined resistance of resistors in series is the sum of the resistances. This is easily proven, by applying conservation of energy and charge to the circuit shown. The same current, I, flows through each of the resistors (due to conservation of charge) and the cell provides a pd of E.

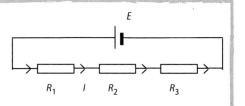

From conservation of energy (or simply adding the pds across the components)

$$E = IR_1 + IR_2 + IR_3$$

factorising I gives: $E = I(R_1 + R_2 + R_3)$

It should be clear that the resistance of the whole circuit is $R_1 + R_2 + R_3$

In parallel

The combined resistance of resistors in parallel is given by the equation

$$\frac{1}{R} = \frac{1}{R_1} + \frac{1}{R_2} + \frac{1}{R_3} + \dots$$

This is proven in a similar manner:

By applying conservation of energy and charge you get

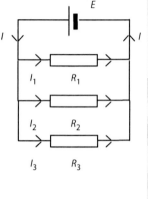

$$I = I_1 + I_2 + I_3$$

and $\qquad E = I_1 R_1 = I_2 R_2 = I_3 R_3$

If you rearrange the last equations you get

$$I_1 = \frac{E}{R_1} \text{ and } I_2 = \frac{E}{R_2} \text{ and } I_3 = \frac{E}{R_3}$$

Now you need to substitute these into the first equation

$$I = I_1 + I_2 + I_3 = \frac{E}{R_1} + \frac{E}{R_2} + \frac{E}{R_3}$$

Finally, all you have to do is factorise the E

$$I = \frac{E}{R_1} + \frac{E}{R_2} + \frac{E}{R_3} = E\left(\frac{1}{R_1} + \frac{1}{R_2} + \frac{1}{R_3}\right)$$

Hence, we've shown that the equation is correct for three resistors in parallel.

Example

Calculate the resistance of the combination

Answer

First calculate the resistance of the three resistors in parallel

$$\frac{1}{R} = \frac{1}{22} + \frac{1}{22} + \frac{1}{22} = \frac{3}{22}$$

$$R = \frac{22}{3} = 7.3 \, \Omega$$

Finally add the other resistor which is in series, resistance = 22 + 7.3 = 29.3 Ω

» Pointer

When two equal resistors are in parallel, the resistance of the combination is half the value of the resistors. When three equal resistors are in parallel the resistance of the combination is a third of the value of the resistors and so on.

quickfire

⑥₁ Calculate the resistance of the combination.

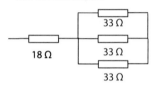

quickfire

⑥₂ Calculate the resistance of the combination.

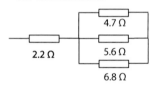

▲ Grade boost

Don't forget to turn your answer upside down at the end of a parallel resistor calculation otherwise your answer is likely to be nonsense.

Potential divider

This following derivation for the output pd of a potential divider is one that you need to remember according to the syllabus.

Because the current I is the same in both resistors, you can write

$$V_{IN} = IR_1 + IR_2$$

and $\qquad V_{OUT} = IR_2$

Dividing the two equations gives

$$\frac{V_{OUT}}{V_{IN}} = \frac{IR_2}{IR_1 + IR_2}$$

cancelling the I,

$$\frac{V_{OUT}}{V_{IN}} = \frac{R_2}{R_1 + R_2}$$

Another way of looking at this result is that the pd divides in the same ratio as the resistors. This equation appears slightly differently on the WJEC data sheet:

$$\frac{V}{V_{TOTAL}} \left(or\ \frac{V_{OUT}}{V_{IN}} \right) = \frac{R}{R_{TOTAL}}$$

Unfortunately, potential divider-based exam questions tend not to be easy. They start off with a simple potential divider then put another resistor (or something similar) across the output resistor (R_2 above).

Example

Calculate the output pd. (This is the easy start!)

Answer

$$\frac{V_{OUT}}{12} = \frac{27}{56 + 27} \rightarrow V_{OUT} = \frac{27}{56 + 27} \times 12$$

$$V_{OUT} = 3.9\ V$$

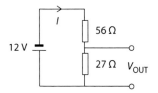

Example

Calculate the current in the 120 Ω resistor (which is trickier).

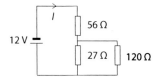

Answer

First you must find the resistance of the 27 Ω resistor in parallel with the 120 Ω resistor.

$$\frac{1}{R} = \frac{1}{R_1} + \frac{1}{R_2} = \frac{1}{27} + \frac{1}{120} = 0.045$$

Grade boost

quickfire

㊳ Calculate the output pd.

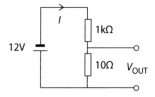

quickfire

㉞ Calculate the value of the resistor that ensures the bulb operates at the correct power. (Hint: calculate the current in the bulb first, then use the fact that you have 6 V across the 27 Ω resistor.)

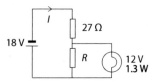

$$R = \frac{1}{0.045} = 22\ \Omega \qquad \text{(this first step is essential)}.$$

Having done the essential first step there are many ways to get the correct answer but here's one method.

The resistance of the whole circuit is $= 22 + 56 = 78\ \Omega$

Apply $I = \dfrac{V}{R}$ to the whole circuit, $I = \dfrac{V}{R} = \dfrac{12}{78} = 0.154$ A

and this is also the current in the 56 Ω resistor.

Now apply $V = IR$ to the 56 Ω resistor $\qquad V = IR = 56 \times 0.154 = 8.6$ V

Finally, you need to apply $I = \dfrac{V}{R}$ to the 120 Ω resistor but first realise that the pd across the two parallel resistors is $12 - 8.6 = 3.4$V

$$I = \frac{V}{R} = \frac{3.4}{120} = 0.028 \text{ A (or 28 mA)}$$

This type of question is asked regularly on the PH1 exam paper. It is often one of the most difficult questions on the paper – be sure that you are completely familiar with this type of DC circuit analysis.

Here are some interesting observations related to the last example that might help you understand the circuit better:

1 Whenever two resistors are in parallel, their combined resistance is always smaller than the smallest resistor i.e. the combined resistance above is 22 Ω and the smallest resistance was 27 Ω.

2 It was possible to obtain the same answers by taking the circuit as a potential divider with the upper resistor as 56 Ω and the lower resistor as 22 Ω.

Then $\dfrac{V}{V_{TOTAL}} \left(\text{or } \dfrac{V_{OUT}}{V_{IN}} \right) = \dfrac{R}{R_{TOTAL}} = \dfrac{22}{78}$, etc.

3 Most wrong answers simply assume that the potential divider still provides the same pd as earlier (i.e. 3.9 V). However, the actual pd across the 120 Ω resistor is lower (3.4 V).

EMF and internal resistance of a cell

The EMF of a cell stands for the electromotive force of a cell. Its definition appears in the key term and is regularly requested in exam papers, so learn it. You can measure the EMF of a cell

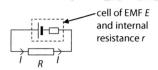

cell of EMF E and internal resistance r

easily; just measure the pd across its terminals when it's not supplying a current. The reason why you have to measure the EMF when the cell is not supplying current becomes more apparent when you apply conservation of energy to a simple circuit involving a real cell with internal resistance r.

Applying conservation of energy, you get:

$$E = IR + Ir$$

but IR is the pd supplied to the external circuit and is often quoted as V

$E = V + Ir$ or $V = E - Ir$ as it appears in the WJEC data sheet.

Sometimes the examiner likes to ask what the above equation means in terms of energy and the answer is this:

E is the energy converted in the cell from chemical to electrical potential energy per coulomb (nearly all cells convert chemical energy to EPE). You could also say that E is the energy dissipated in the whole circuit per coulomb.

IR or V is the energy dissipated in the resistor R per coulomb. Alternatively, it is the energy dissipated in the external circuit per coulomb.

Ir is the energy dissipated in the cell (or internal resistance) per coulomb

When this question is asked it's usually worth 4 marks which is about half a grade.

Example
A cell has an EMF of 1.63 V and an internal resistance of 0.23 Ω. Calculate the current when the cell is connected to a resistor of 8.2 Ω.

Answer
total resistance = 8.2 + 0.23 = 8.43 Ω
$$I = \frac{V}{R} = \frac{1.63}{8.43} = 0.193 \text{ A (or 193 mA)}$$
alternatively, you can factorise I in $E = IR + Ir = I(R + r)$ but this is exactly equivalent.

Example
What is the current when two identical cells of EMF 1.63 V and internal resistance 0.23 Ω are connected in series to a resistor of 8.2 Ω?

Answer
total resistance = 8.2 + 0.23 + 0.23 = 8.66Ω

total EMF = 1.63 × 2 = 3.26 V
$$I = \frac{V}{R} = \frac{3.26}{8.66} = 0.376 \text{ A (or 376 mA)}$$
In the equation $V = E - Ir$, V is the pd across the resistor and E is the EMF of the cell. However, you should also note that V is the pd across the terminals of the cell. Because V is less than the EMF of the cell by the amount Ir, the value Ir is sometimes called 'the lost volts'.

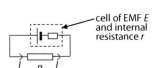
cell of EMF E and internal resistance r

≫ Pointer
A common wrong answer would be to multiply the previous answer by 2, i.e. 193 mA × 2 = 386 mA. This is wrong because, although the EMF has doubled, you also have a slight increase in the resistance (8.23 Ω to 8.66 Ω).

≫ Pointer
A very cheeky correct answer here is that the current is zero. Have a look at the circuit below. The total EMF of the circuit is zero (opposing cells) so the current must be zero.

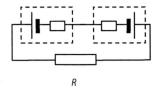
R

Grade boost

Even if there are cheeky ways of obtaining a correct answer don't bother looking for them, just do what you think the examiner wants you to do.

quickfire

65 A voltage/current graph for a cell has intercept 1.65 V and gradient – 2.5 Ω. Find the EMF, internal resistance and maximum current which the cell can supply.

Another source of questions is the graph of V against I. This is achieved in practice using the following apparatus. The graph of results would be:

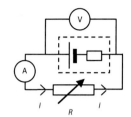

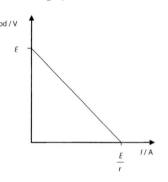

comparing the equation $V = E - Ir$ with $y = mx + c$, you should notice that the gradient is $-r$ and that the intercept (when I is zero) is E. Also, a little algebra will show you that the maximum current (when $R = 0$) is $I = \dfrac{E}{r}$.

Summary: PH1 Motion, Energy and Charge

Basic physics

- Units – SI and checking equations
- Scalars and vectors (including adding and resolving vectors)
- Force – Newton's 3rd law and $\sum F = ma$
- Density $\rho = \dfrac{m}{v}$
- Moments (force × perpendicular distance) and principle of moments
- Conditions for equilibrium ($\sum F = 0$ and sum of moments = 0)

Energy concepts

- Work (definition and use of equation, $W = Fx \cos\theta$)
- Hooke's law and area under Force–distance graph $\left(F = kx, \ E = \dfrac{1}{2}Fx, \text{etc.} \right)$
- Work–energy relationship $\left(Fs = \dfrac{1}{2}mv^2 - \dfrac{1}{2}mu^2 \right)$, kinetic energy, gravitational potential energy and conservation of energy
- Power, efficiency and dissipative forces

Resistance

- Definition of pd (in terms of energy per C), Ohm's law, resistance and $V = IR$
- $I - V$ graphs for a diode, filament and metal wire
- Resistivity $\left(R = \dfrac{\rho l}{A} \right)$ and the experiment to measure it
- Variation of resistance with temperature and the experiment to demonstrate it
- Superconductivity, the transition temperature and superconductor applications
- Electrical power $$P = IV = I^2R = \dfrac{V^2}{R}$$

Kinematics

- Definitions of velocity, speed, acceleration, displacement, etc.
- Graphs of distance–time, velocity–time and acceleration–time
- Uniform acceleration equations ($v = u + at$), etc.
- Terminal velocity and air resistance
- Projectile motion (constant horizontal velocity, vertical acceleration = g)

Conduction of electricity

- Charging insulators using friction and the movement of negative electrons
- Unit of charge (C), the charge on an electron (1.6×10^{-19} C) and the coulomb meter
- Current $\left(I = \dfrac{\Delta Q}{\Delta t} \right)$, drift velocity, deriving and using $I = nAve$

DC circuits

- Conservation of charge and energy in circuits and their consequences
- Derive and use potential divider formula $$\dfrac{V}{V_{total}} \left(\text{or} \ \dfrac{V_{OUT}}{V_{IN}} \right) = \dfrac{R}{R_{total}}$$
- Define EMF (in terms of energy per C)
- Use of the formula $V = E - Ir$ for real cells with internal resistance r

Knowledge and Understanding

PH2 Waves and Particles

The main theme of PH2 is the nature of light. In many ways it behaves as a wave, showing the wave properties of polarisation, interference, diffraction, refraction and reflection. (At this point we look at a significant application: optical fibres.) A purely wave theory of light fails to explain the details of the photoelectric effect. We have to accept that light energy is quantised into packets or 'photons'. This helps us to understand how lasers work and how atomic spectra arise. We learn a great deal about *stars* from their spectra. To understand the processes by which energy is liberated in a star, we need ideas about fundamental particles and forces.

Revision checklist

Tick column 1 when you have completed brief revision notes.

Tick column 2 when you think you have a good grasp of the topic.

Tick column 3 during final revision when you feel you have mastered the topic.

		1	2	3	Notes
p66	**Waves**				
p66	How waves travel				
p68	Wavefront diagrams				
p69	Waves changing medium				
p73	Fibre optics				
p74	Interference				
p75	Young's *Fringes* experiment				
p76	Accurate measurement of wavelength				
p76	The diffraction grating				
p78	Stationary (standing) waves				
p80	The electromagnetic (e-m) spectrum				
p81	Electromagnetic (e-m) waves and polarisation				
p83	**Photons**				
p83	Photons				
p84	The photoelectric effect				
p87	Atomic line emission spectra				
p88	Atomic line absorption spectra				
p89	Lasers				
p92	**The particle nature of matter**				
p92	Atoms				
p93	Quarks, leptons and generations				

Longitudinal wave
= where the particle oscillations are in line with (parallel to) the direction of travel (or 'propagation') of the wave.

Transverse wave = where the particle oscillations are at right angles to the direction of travel (or propagation) of the wave.

Waves

How waves travel?

A progressive wave (usually just called a wave) is a disturbance which travels through a medium. Example: air is a medium for sound waves.

The wave source is usually an oscillating (vibrating) object in contact with the medium. This source keeps the particles of the medium next to it oscillating. These particles pass the oscillations to their neighbours and so on, so a wave of particle disturbance propagates (travels) through the medium, taking energy with it.

Longitudinal waves

Examples: sound, earthquake 'P' waves, 'compression' waves in a 'Slinky' spring (below).

>> *Pointer*

The particles in a wave don't *travel*. They never really get anywhere, just oscillating about their usual positions.

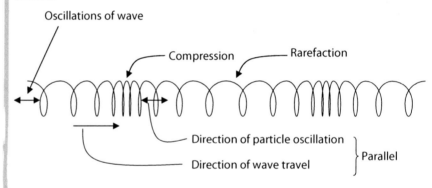

Diagram: Transverse waves

Examples are light (and other electromagnetic waves), Earthquake 'S' waves, waves in a stretched string (below).

>> *Pointer*

Electromagnetic waves are special. They don't need a medium, and can travel in a vacuum, where their speed is $3.00 \times 10^8 \, \text{m s}^{-1}$. [Their speed in air is the same, to 3 sig. figs.]
   The oscillations are not those of particles, but of electric and magnetic fields. We usually show the direction of the electric field only.

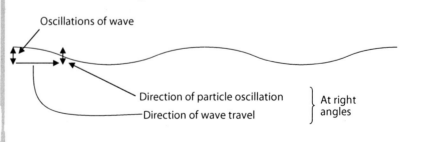

Polarisation of transverse waves

The wave shown in the last diagram is polarised (strictly, linearly polarised). This means that the particle oscillations are in just one of the many possible directions at right angles to the directions of travel.

Unpolarised waves are transverse waves in which the direction of oscillation keeps changing randomly – but is always at right angles to the direction of travel.

We can sum this up with two diagrams, drawn for waves travelling out of the page towards you. The arrows are oscillation directions.

Polarised   Unpolarised

An oscillating particle

Consider one particle of the medium in the path of a wave. Its displacement from its undisturbed position may vary with time like this:

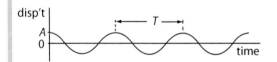

A = amplitude
= maximum displacement

T = period (periodic time)
= time for one cycle

The **frequency**, f, is the number of cycles per unit time. Unit: s^{-1} = hertz (Hz). For example if $T = 0.10$ s, then $f = 10$ Hz. The relationship is

$$f = \frac{1}{T} \quad \text{which can be rearranged as} \quad T = \frac{1}{f}.$$

A snapshot of a wave

The graph shows the displacement of particles of the medium in the path of the wave at one particular time.

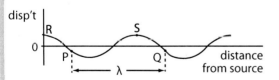

λ = wavelength
= **distance between** consecutive particles oscillating in phase

Particle Q is oscillating **in phase** with particle P. This means that P and Q are at the same point in their oscillation cycles at the same time. Another example of in-phase particles is the pair R and S.

Key Terms

Amplitude = the maximum value of the displacement of an oscillating particle from its equilibrium position.

Period = the time taken for one complete cycle of oscillation.

Frequency = the number of cycles of a wave that pass a given point in one second (or equivalently the number of cycles of oscillation per second performed by any particle in the medium).

In phase = at the same point in their oscillation cycles at the same time.

Wavelength = the minimum distance (measured along the direction of propagation) between two points on the wave oscillating in phase.

Grade boost

Make sure you can write out the definitions of polarised and unpolarised transverse waves.

 quickfire

① An oscillating particle does 3000 cycles in a minute. What (in SI units) is:
- its frequency?
- its period?

Key Term

Diffraction = the spreading of waves when they meet obstacles, such as the edges of a slit. Some of the wave's energy travels into the geometrical shadows of the obstacles.

» Pointer

Always check what is being plotted on the 'x'-axis!

» Pointer

The *frequency*, *f*, of the waves is that of the *source*. The wave *speed*, *v*, is usually set by the medium.

» Pointer

For waves spreading 2- or 3-dimensionally from a small source, amplitude falls with distance.

② In a water wave a peak and the nearest trough are 2.0 m apart. 90 peaks pass a stationary observer per minute. Calculate the wave speed.

Grade boost

When drawing wavefront diagrams, don't let λ change (unless the medium changes – see later)

Speed of a wave

Look first at the full line 'snapshot' in the graph below.

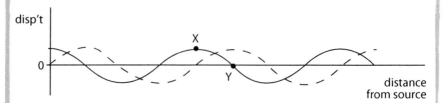

Particle Y is λ/4 further from the wave source than particle X. Its oscillations lag behind X's by a quarter of a cycle. Time *T*/4 later, X will have gone from peak to zero displacement, and Y from zero to peak. Thus we get the broken line, showing the particles' displacements at a time *T*/4 later. The wave has moved forward by λ/4. In time *T* it will have moved forward by λ.

So, wave speed, $v = \dfrac{\text{distance gone}}{\text{time taken}} = \dfrac{\lambda}{T} = \dfrac{1}{T} \times \lambda.$ So $v = f\lambda.$

Wavefront diagrams

The first two diagrams below are for waves travelling 2 dimensionally (as ripples on a pond appear to do) or 3 dimensionally, like light and sound.

- The equally spaced lines (or curves) on the next two diagrams are wavefronts: all particles on any wavefront are oscillating in phase.
- We usually draw wavefronts at intervals of one wavelength – like the peaks (crests) of a water wave.
- The direction of travel of a wave at any point is at right angles to the wavefront through that point.

Diffraction

This is the spreading of waves around obstacles – such as the walls at either side of a slit …

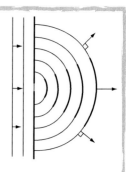

Slit width ≤ λ

In this case, the wave spreads right round through 90° each side of the straight-through direction (though the amplitude is less at the sides). See top right diagram.

Slit width > λ

In this case there is a main or central beam, which doesn't spread all round. There are also 'side beams' of much lower amplitude.

The wider the slit the greater the amplitude of the main beam, but the less its angular spread.

The diffraction of light can be demonstrated like this:

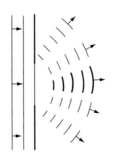

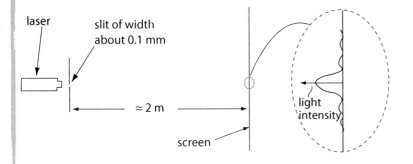

Where the intensity is greatest, so is the wave amplitude. Note the exaggerated scale of distances up and down the screen; the light spreads only through a very small angle. This is because the wavelength of the light will be around 600 nm, so the slit is over 100 wavelengths wide!

Waves changing medium

Speed, frequency and wavelength

The speed of a wave is usually determined by the medium in which it is travelling. For example, at 20°C, sound travels 4.3 times faster in water than in air.

Suppose a wave passes from medium 1, in which its speed is v_1, to medium 2 (speed v_2).

Its *frequency* will stay the same (that of the source), as each cycle is passed across the interface between 1 and 2.

So, using $v = f\lambda$, $f = \dfrac{v_1}{\lambda_1} = \dfrac{v_2}{\lambda_2}$.

Re-arranging: $\dfrac{\lambda_1}{\lambda_2} = \dfrac{v_1}{v_2}$.

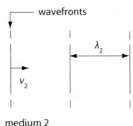

wavefronts

medium 1   medium 2

Pointer

It's also diffraction when waves in the sea come together on the far side of a rock.

quickfire

③ Why can you hear someone through an open door, when you can't see them? [Hint: a typical wavelength for sound is 1 m.]

quickfire

④ Suggest why reception of vhf radio signals (frequency around 100 MHz) is often poor in deep, narrow valleys, whereas for 'long wave' (frequency < 1 MHz) reception is fine.

quickfire

⑤ A whistle is blown above water. The wavelength of the sound is 0.20 m in air. What is it in the water? (The speed is 4.3 times greater.)

Refraction = when a wave passes obliquely from one medium to another its direction of travel changes.

Refractive index = see equation in text.

≫ Pointer

The exam won't ask you to *derive*

$$\frac{\sin \theta_1}{\sin \theta_2} = \frac{v_1}{v_2}.$$

quickfire

⑥ A water wave travelling at 3.0 m s^{-1} meets a boundary with deeper water. The incident and refracted waves travel at 30° and 42° to the normal. Calculate the speed of the wave on the deeper water.

≫ Pointer

There is also some reflection at a boundary.

quickfire

⑦ Calculate the speed of light in water (n = 1.33).

≫ Pointer

Because v_1 and v_2, (or n_1 and n_2) are constants for the media 1 and 2, then $\dfrac{\sin \theta_1}{\sin \theta_2}$ is a constant.

This is **Snell's Law**.
It is confirmed by experiment.

Refraction

If a wave passes obliquely from one medium to another its direction of travel changes. This is **refraction**.

If $v_2 > v_1$, the direction of travel bends away from the normal (the line at right angles to the boundary), as light goes from medium 1 to medium 2.

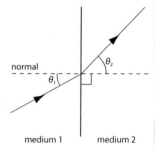

The lower diagram shows a wide 'beam' of waves. Wavefronts AB and CD are drawn at right angles to the directions of travel in medium 1 and medium 2. In fact CD is a later position of AB.

We can now see why the direction of travel *must* change in this way. While end A of AB is still travelling at speed v_1 to C, end B is travelling at speed v_2 to D, so BD > AC.

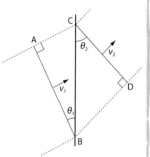

Taking this further, suppose t is the time for AB to reach CD. Then AC = $v_1 t$ and BD = $v_2 t$. Using the two right-angled triangles, ABC and DCB:

$$\sin \theta_1 = \frac{AC}{BC} = \frac{v_1 t}{BC}; \quad \sin \theta_2 = \frac{DB}{BC} = \frac{v_2 t}{BC}. \quad \text{By division:} \quad \frac{\sin \theta_1}{\sin \theta_2} = \frac{v_1}{v_2}$$

It's not hard to show that the angles marked θ_1 in the upper and lower diagrams are equal. The same goes for the angles θ_2.

Refraction of light

Light travels more slowly in transparent material media than in a vacuum. We define the **refractive index**, n, of a medium as

$$n = \frac{\text{speed of light in a vacuum}}{\text{speed of light in the medium}}, \quad \text{that is} \quad n = \frac{c}{v}.$$

Examples: for air n = 1.00, for water n = 1.33, for ordinary glass, n = 1.52.

Because $nv = c$, if we compare two media (medium 1 and medium 2):

$$n_1 v_1 = n_2 v_2, \quad \text{that is} \quad \frac{v_1}{v_2} = \frac{n_2}{n_1}.$$

We can now write the wave refraction equation in terms of n_1 and n_2:

$$\frac{\sin \theta_1}{\sin \theta_2} = \frac{v_1}{v_2} \quad \text{is equivalent to} \quad \frac{\sin \theta_1}{\sin \theta_2} = \frac{n_2}{n_1}.$$

Or, more memorably: $n_1 \sin \theta_1 = n_2 \sin \theta_2$

Light paths are *reversible* (see diagram, which is drawn for the case $n_2 > n_1$), so the equation works whether light is going from medium 1 to medium 2 or vice versa.

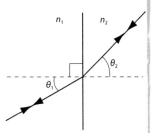

Example

A laser beam is shone into a fish-tank through one of its glass walls, as shown. Angle θ_a is 45°. Find the angles θ_g and θ_w. (Note that the two angles marked θ_g are equal only because the glass wall of the fish-tank has parallel faces.)

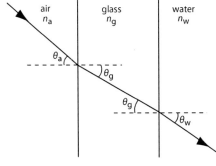

At the air-glass boundary,

$$n_a \sin \theta_a = n_g \sin \theta_g \quad \text{so} \quad 1.00 \sin 45° = 1.52 \sin \theta_g.$$

So $\sin \theta_g = \dfrac{1.00 \sin 45°}{1.52} = 0.465$ so $\theta_g = \sin^{-1} 0.465 = 28°$

At the glass-water boundary,

$$n_g \sin \theta_g = n_w \sin \theta_w \quad \text{so} \quad 1.52 \times 0.465 = 1.33 \sin \theta_w.$$

So $\sin \theta_w = \dfrac{1.52 \times 0.465}{1.33} = 0.532$ so $\theta_w = \sin^{-1} 0.532 = 32°$

⊙◀◀◀◀ quickfire

⑧ For light passing *directly* from air to water, with $\theta_a = 45°$, find θ_w.

Sketching paths of refracted light

Draw a normal wherever the light beam hits a boundary. Light bends away from the normal when it goes into a medium of smaller refractive index (where it travels faster), and towards the normal when it goes into a medium of greater index.

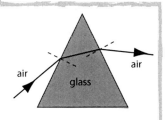

>> **Pointer**

The reflection is said to be *internal* because medium 1 is often a solid (like glass) and medium 2 is often just air.

quickfire

⑨ Calculate the critical angle for light going from diamond ($n = 2.42$) to air.

Grade boost

Check that you can sketch light paths through glass blocks of simple shapes. In an exam you'll be given enough information to work out if total internal reflection occurs.

Critical angle

Consider a light beam travelling in a medium (1) and approaching a medium (2) with smaller refractive index, in which the light travels faster (e.g. light approaching air from glass).

In the top diagram, where θ_1 is smallish, the light bends away from the normal, as you should expect!

Note that some of the light is reflected back into medium 1 (partial reflection). The angles of incidence and reflection (that is the angles of the beams to the normal) are equal.

If we increase θ_1, it is going to reach a value, C, called the **critical angle for light going from medium 1 to medium 2 ($n_1 > n_2$)**, at which θ_2 is 90° (middle diagram).

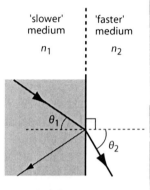

'slower' medium n_1 | 'faster' medium n_2

In this case $n_1 \sin C = n_2 \sin 90°$.

But $\sin 90° = 1$, so $n_1 \sin C = n_2$

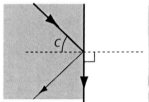

Example

Calculate the critical angle for light approaching water from glass.

$n_g \sin \theta_g = n_w \sin \theta_w$ so $1.52 \sin C = 1.33 \sin 90°$

so $\sin C = \dfrac{1.33 \times 1}{1.52} = 0.875$ so $C = \sin^{-1} 0.875$

$= 61°$

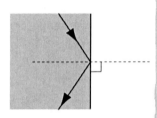

Total internal reflection

When $\theta_1 > C$, the refraction equation gives $\sin \theta_2 > 1$ which is absurd, because there is no value of θ_2 for which $\sin \theta_2 > 1$. The equation simply doesn't apply when $\theta_1 > C$. In fact *no* light enters medium 2. The light is **totally internally reflected** (at an equal angle) back into medium 1. See third diagram.

Total internal reflection is the effect which gives diamonds their sparkle. It is also used instead of mirrors in high class optical instruments such as prism binoculars. We home in on its use in fibre optics.

Fibre optics

An optical fibre is a long, thin, cylindrical core of glass, encased in a cladding of glass of lower refractive index.

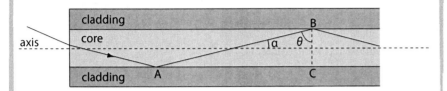

Suppose light enters the core at one end, and travels at an angle α to the axis. If α is small enough, the light will strike the core/cladding boundary at an angle θ (to the normal) greater than the critical angle. Then the light will totally internally reflect back into the core, and will carry on along the fibre in a zigzag path without escaping.

This will still happen if the fibre is bent into a curve. Optical fibres can therefore take light to rather inaccessible places (such as the stomach).

Carrying data in optical fibres

Data can be *encoded*, as a sequence of pulses, in light from a laser, and sent along a fibre. In very pure glass the light 'signal' goes many kilometres without needing a boost – unlike a signal sent by currents in copper wires. These also suffer 'cross-talk' from other wires, whereas fibres (in opaque sheets) are almost immune from outside influences.

Multimode dispersion

Light going along the axis ($\alpha = 0$) takes the shortest time to travel a given length, L, of fibre. Zigzag paths take longer. A single pulse of data travels the length L by many paths of different lengths and arrives spread out over a longer time than the initial pulse duration. This 'pulse-broadening' effect is called **multimode dispersion**.

Data is usually sent at a rapid rate (very small intervals between pulses), so, if the fibre is long, pulse-broadening might cause pulses to overlap. This limits the use of these 'step index' **multimode fibres** to short lengths.

For long distance data transport, **monomode fibres** are used. These have very thin cores (a few wavelengths in diameter). In these fibres there are no zigzag paths; light can only travel parallel to the axis. So there is no multimode dispersion. [The reason is beyond A-level!]

Key Terms

Multimode fibre = optical fibre with large core diameter. Light can travel along it by many different routes, involving reflections from the side.

Multimode dispersion = see main text.

Monomode fibre = optical fibre with diameter only a few wavelengths of light, in which light can only travel via one path – parallel to the axis.

quickfire

⑩ If n_{core} = 1.62 and n_{clad} = 1.52, calculate the critical angle at the core/cladding boundary.

quickfire

⑪ What, then, is the largest angle *to the axis* at which light can travel long distances in the core?

quickfire

⑫ Calculate the time for a pulse of light to travel 2.5 km parallel to the axis of a fibre for which n_{core} = 1.62.

quickfire

⑬ Repeat, but for light taking a zigzag path for which $\alpha = 10°$. Hint: Consider the triangle ABC.

Principle of superposition = When waves from two (or more) sources travel through the same region, the resultant displacement at any point is the vector sum of the displacements of the individual waves.

Constructive and destructive interference = see main text.

Interference

The diagram shows wavefronts arising from S_1 and S_2, two in-phase sources, (sources oscillating in phase). There are 'beams' of high amplitude separated by 'channels' of zero (or almost zero) amplitude. We explain this pattern using the principle of superposition.

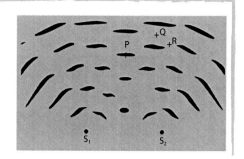

≫ *Pointer*

'*Vector* sum' implies that equal and opposite displacements will add to zero.

This can't happen for two displacements at right angles. So, for polarised waves, the vibration directions mustn't be at right angles if the waves are to produce an interference pattern.

The principle of superposition

When waves from two (or more) sources travel through the same region, the resultant displacement at any point is the vector sum of the displacements of the individual waves.

Constructive and destructive interference

Where the amplitude is highest (e.g. at P or Q) the waves from the slits are arriving in phase, and interfering constructively (see alongside).

Where the amplitude is lowest (e.g. at R), the waves are arriving in anti-phase and interfering destructively (see alongside).

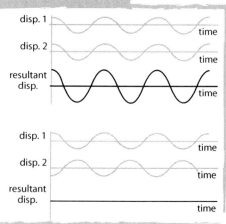

≫ *Pointer*

Q in the top diagram does have maximum amplitude, even though the displacement may be zero at the instant for which the diagram is drawn.

Path difference

There is constructive interference at P in the top diagram, because, to get to P, the waves from S_1 and S_2 travel along paths, S_1P and S_2P, of equal length, and so arrive at P in phase.

For point Q, the paths are S_1Q, and S_2Q. The path difference, $S_1Q - S_2Q$, is 1 wavelength, so waves from S_1 arrive at Q one whole cycle later than those from S_2 – which means they arrive at Q in phase with waves from S_2!

The general rule, for waves from in-phase source, is:

For constructive interference at a point X,

path difference, $S_1X - S_2X = 0$, or λ, or 2λ, or $3\lambda \ldots$

For destructive interference at a point X,

path difference, $S_1X - S_2X = \dfrac{1}{2}\lambda$ or $\dfrac{3}{2}\lambda$ or $\dfrac{5}{2}\lambda \ldots$

quickfire

⑭ What, in terms of wavelength, is the path difference $S_1R - S_2R$?

Young's *Fringes* experiment

In the early 1800s, Thomas Young investigated the light passing through two parallel slits close together. He observed a pattern of bright and dark *fringes* (stripes) on a screen placed in front of the slits. He recognized this as part of an interference pattern, and deduced that light was wave-like. Here is a modern version of his experiment…

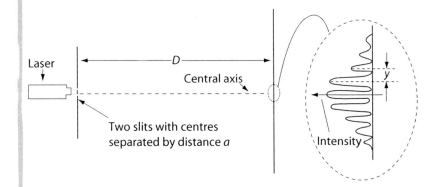

quickfire

⑮ Why does the fringe intensity fall off with distance from the central axis? [Hint: at greater distances from the central axis, fringes reappear, but faintly.]

With $a = 0.50$ mm and $D = 2.0$ m, and using red light, the fringe separation, y, (between centres of bright fringes) is roughly 2.5 mm.

The role of diffraction

Light passing through each slit diffracts slightly, so there is a (smallish) region where the light from each slit overlaps – and interferes.

quickfire

⑯ Suppose $D = 2.0$ m, $a = 0.50$ mm, and y is found to be 2.5 mm. Calculate λ.

The Young's fringes formula

The wavelength of the light can be found from the formula

$$\lambda = \frac{ay}{D}$$

This is an approximation based on the path difference rule for constructive interference. As long as $a << D$ and $y << D$ the formula is almost exact.

≫ Pointer

When we illuminate the two slits with light from a laser, the two slits might well not be in-phase sources. But they will be coherent: there will be a constant phase difference between them.

Key Terms

Monochromatic light = continuous oscillations of almost a single frequency.

Coherent light = monochromatic light with wavefronts continuous across the beam.

Coherent sources = Wave sources which have a constant phase difference between them (and therefore must have the same frequency).

Diffraction grating = a flat plate which is opaque except for thousands of straight parallel, equally spaced slits.

Coherence

If we illuminate the two slits with light from different sources, we can never produce fringes. Even using a single 'ordinary' source such as an LED we can produce fringes only by taking special precautions. But, using a laser, the simple arrangement above gives clear fringes. This is because a laser produces coherent light:

- Laser light is almost **monochromatic**: continuous oscillations of almost a single frequency. (Light from a red LED is a sum of oscillations with a range of frequencies.)
- The laser beam has wavefronts which stretch right across its width.

This is not so for an LED or a filament lamp. If we simply substituted one of these for the laser in the Young's fringes set-up above, the slits would act as incoherent sources: there'd be no constant phase relationship between them – and no fringes!

quickfire

⑰ If the slits act as sources in anti-phase, would we still see fringes?

Accurate measurement of wavelength

Physicists need to measure wavelengths accurately, for example when trying to identify atoms in a star's atmosphere by the light they absorb and emit. Young's fringes would be too inaccurate because:

- The fringes are not sharp: bright fringes fade gradually into dark.
- The 'bright' fringes are therefore not very bright.
- The fringe separation is small.

All three issues are addressed by the diffraction grating.

The diffraction grating

At its simplest, this is a flat plate which is opaque except for thousands of straight parallel, equally spaced slits.

The slits are very narrow (in the order of a wavelength wide) so, when light is incident on the grating, the diffracted waves spread 'right round'. The waves from different slits interfere to produce beams.

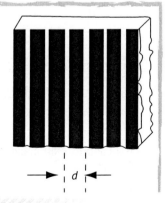

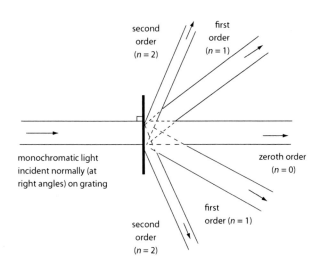

second order (n = 2)
first order (n = 1)
monochromatic light incident normally (at right angles) on grating
zeroth order (n = 0)
first order (n = 1)
second order (n = 2)

The beams correspond to those which give the bright fringes in Young's two slit experiment, but they are much further apart, because the slits are much closer together. The beams are also bright and well defined, separated by dark areas of almost total destructive interference.

(If the beams fall on a screen they produce bright spots in a line. If the light source is a distant slit, illuminated with monochromatic light and parallel to the slits in the grating, the dots are replaced by lines, which is why a monochromatic light source is said to have a 'line spectrum'.)

The grating equation

The wavelength of the light can be found from the *grating equation*

$$n\lambda = d \sin\theta$$

d is the separation of the centres of adjacent slits. Its value (or the number of slits per metre) is supplied by the grating's maker.

θ is the angle to the normal of either of the two n^{th} order beams. To find λ, we can measure θ for any order (except zeroth).

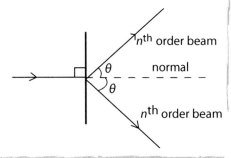

n^{th} order beam
normal
θ
θ
n^{th} order beam

Grade boost

Note carefully the way the beams from the grating are labelled.

Pointer

There may be more (or fewer) orders than those shown on the diagram. (See next page.)

Grade boost

Suppose the highest order beam produced is the second (n = 2). Then 5 beams will emerge altogether. Don't confuse number or orders with number of beams.

Pointer

$d \sin\theta$ in the grating equation is, in fact, the effective *path difference* between light leaving at angle θ from adjacent slits.

quickfire

⑱ Calculate *d* for a grating with 500 slits per millimetre of its width.

Example

A diffraction grating has 400 slits per millimetre. Light from a street lamp produces third order beams at 45.0° either side of the normal.

(a) Determine the wavelength of the light.

(b) Find the highest order produced.

⑲ Suppose we find that monochromatic light shone normally on the grating of QF18 gives second order beams at 36° to the normal. Calculate λ.

⑳ How many orders will there be for the grating of QF18 and this wavelength of light?

Answer

(a) First we note that since there are 400 slits per millimetre, then

$$d = \frac{1}{400}\,\text{mm} = 2.5 \times 10^{-3}\,\text{mm} = 2.5 \times 10^{-6}\,\text{m}$$

Now we can use the grating equation:

$$\lambda = \frac{d\sin\theta}{n} = \frac{2.5 \times 10^{-6}\,\text{m} \times \sin 45°}{3} = 5.9 \times 10^{-7}\,\text{m}$$

(b) One way to do this is to re-arrange the grating equation as $n = \frac{d\sin\theta}{\lambda}$

Sin θ can't be greater than 1, so $n \leq \frac{d}{\lambda}$. In this case $n \leq \frac{2.5 \times 10^{-6}\,\text{m}}{5.9 \times 10^{-7}\,\text{m}}$.

Doing the division, we find $n \leq 4.2$, so the maximum number of orders is 4.

Stationary (standing) waves

These can be set up on a stretched string, as shown, and viewed in slow motion with a stroboscope (light flashing at regular intervals).

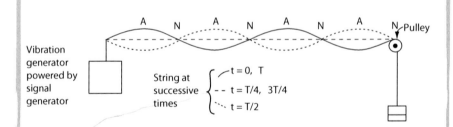

Characteristic features of stationary waves:

- The amplitude of the oscillations varies cyclically with distance, dropping to zero at **nodes** (N) and rising to a maximum at **antinodes** (A).
- Between one node and the next all particles oscillate in phase, but there is a phase reversal at each node.
- No energy is transported.

Grade boost

Make sure you can contrast in detail the variation with distance of amplitude and phase for standing waves and progressive waves.

Standing waves as interference patterns

When two progressive waves of equal amplitude and frequency, which, individually would be travelling in opposite directions, occupy the same region, they interfere to produce a stationary wave.

In the set-up shown in the last diagram a wave from the vibration generator travels to the right, and a wave reflected from the pulley, to the left.

Antinodes correspond to constructive interference. They are spaced $\lambda/2$ apart (as moving a distance of $\lambda/2$ changes by a whole wavelength the *path difference* between waves coming from one side and waves from the other). Nodes (destructive interference) are also $\lambda/2$ apart.

⊙ ⋘⋘ **quickfire**

㉑ The fundamental frequency of a string of length 1.50 m is 128 Hz. Calculate the speed of transverse waves on the string.

Stationary waves on strings fixed at both ends

Since there must be nodes at each end, the string can vibrate in only certain *modes*. The three lowest frequency modes are shown:

FUNDAMENTAL OR FIRST HARMONIC	SECOND HARMONIC	THIRD HARMONIC

$$\frac{\lambda}{2} = L \text{ so } \lambda = 2L \qquad \frac{\lambda}{2} = \frac{L}{2} \text{ so } \lambda = \frac{2L}{2} \qquad \frac{\lambda}{2} = \frac{L}{3} \text{ so } \lambda = \frac{2L}{3}$$

$$f = \frac{v}{\lambda} \text{ so } f = \frac{v}{2L} \qquad f = \frac{v}{\lambda} \text{ so } f = \frac{2v}{2L} \qquad f = \frac{v}{\lambda} \text{ so } f = \frac{3v}{2L}$$

v is the speed of transverse waves along the string. (This depends on the mass per unit length of the string, and the tension it is under.)

In *which* mode will the string vibrate? This is determined by whether the string is hit, plucked or bowed, and where on the string this is done. In fact, the string will usually vibrate in a sum of modes!

》 Pointer

For the string fixed at both ends, the frequencies of the modes of vibration are multiples or 'harmonics' of the fundamental frequency, $v/2L$.

Other types of standing wave

Any type of progressive wave can have a corresponding stationary wave.

For stationary sound waves in pipes, there are nodes at closed ends and antinodes at open ends. These stationary waves are responsible for the sounds produced by wind instruments.

⊙ ⋘⋘ **quickfire**

㉒ If a string fixed at both ends is set vibrating by hitting it in the middle, which harmonics *won't* be present in the superposition of modes?

Grade boost

Learn typical wavelengths (or frequencies) for the named regions of the e-m spectrum.

quickfire

㉓ The wavelength of a vhf radio broadcast is greater than the wavelength of visible light by a factor of roughly 5×10^4 or 5×10^5 or 5×10^6?

quickfire

㉔ Suggest what kitchen device uses waves of wavelength 12.5 cm.

quickfire

㉕ State one thing far ultraviolet (that is far from the visible) can do, which infra-red cannot do.

quickfire

㉖ Which of these has/have a line spectrum:

- Light from a laser?
- Light from a filament lamp?
- Radio waves from a radio station?

The electromagnetic (e-m) spectrum

The visible spectrum

A diffraction grating splits 'white light' (e.g. sunlight) into a continuous spectrum of colours. In the first order (and higher orders) these colours of light emerge at different angles, showing that they have different wavelengths. The colours range from dark red ($\lambda \approx 700$ nm) through shades of orange, yellow, green and blue to violet ($\lambda \approx 400$ nm).

The whole spectrum

Our eyes are sensitive to only a tiny slice of the whole spectrum of e-m waves. The other regions of the spectrum were discovered at different times, using different sources, and they overlap. The chart below uses logarithmic scales; tenfold increases are represented by one scale division. Half a division is a factor of $\sqrt{10}$ (about 3).

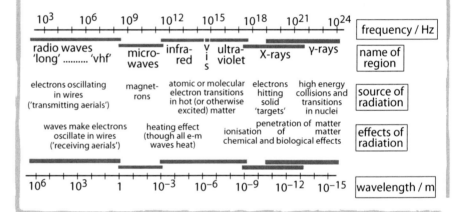

The X-ray spectrum from an X-ray tube

In an X-ray tube, a heated metal 'cathode' emits electrons into a vacuum. The electrons are accelerated towards a metal *target*, by putting a high voltage between target and cathode. When electrons crash into the target, X-rays are emitted. (Most of the electrons' kinetic energy, though, becomes random thermal energy of the target.)

The sketch-graph (also known as a **spectrum**!) shows how the intensity of X-rays from the tube is divided up between different wavelengths (for a particular voltage and target material).

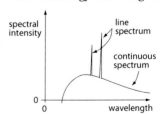

Note the **continuous spectrum**, on which is superimposed a **line spectrum**.

In a line spectrum a very narrow range of wavelengths has much more intensity than neighbouring wavelengths.

Electromagnetic (e-m) waves and polarisation

Oscillating electric field

Charged particles in the path of an e-m wave experience oscillating forces; we say that the wave has an oscillating electric field. [There is a 'companion' oscillating magnetic field which we won't refer to again.] The oscillations are at right angles to the wave's direction of travel.

Grade boost

Make sure you know how polarisation can be shown for both microwaves and light.

Microwaves shown to be transverse

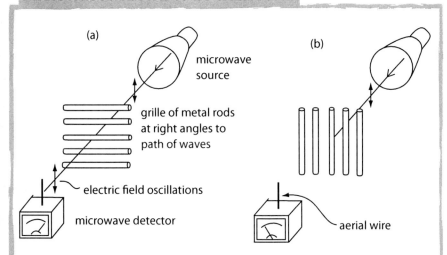

(a)

microwave source

grille of metal rods at right angles to path of waves

electric field oscillations

microwave detector

(b)

aerial wire

Pointer

In microwave set-up (a), the grille lets the waves through to the detector, where their oscillating electric field forces electrons to move up and down the aerial.

In (b), the electric field makes electrons move up and down the rods of the grille, and this results in a reflected wave; very little energy goes through.

E-m waves of wavelength a few centimetres (microwaves) can pass freely through a grille of metal rods (spacing $< \lambda$), when the rods are in one direction. The energy getting through falls gradually to zero as the rods are turned through a right angle. This could not happen unless the waves were transverse and polarised.

» Pointer

Polaroid absorbs, rather than reflects, wave components with an electric field parallel to the molecules. Mobile electrons dissipate energy by collisions as they are forced to move up and down the molecules.

Light shown to be transverse

Polaroid is a man-made material containing long parallel molecules which allow electrons to pass up and down them. It serves the same purpose for light ($\lambda \sim 10^{-6}$ m) as the grille of rods does for microwaves ($\lambda \sim 10^{-2}$ m). Study this sequence of experiments...

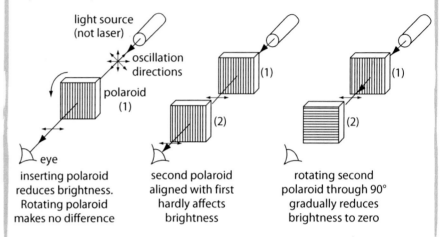

inserting polaroid reduces brightness. Rotating polaroid makes no difference

second polaroid aligned with first hardly affects brightness

rotating second polaroid through 90° gradually reduces brightness to zero

The null effect of rotating the single polaroid shows light from an ordinary source to be unpolarised. The first polaroid allows through only electric field oscillation components perpendicular to its molecules, so it polarises the light. Rotating the second polaroid confirms this.

Photons

Photons

Everything in nature seems to come in lumps or quanta. For example, ordinary matter is made of atoms, and electric charge comes in units of e. This lumpiness was becoming fully accepted only in the early 1900s. In 1905 Einstein boldly suggested that light, too, was lumpy. Light quanta are now called **photons**.

A photon is a discrete packet of electromagnetic (e-m) radiation energy. The energy of a photon is given by:

$$E_{phot} = hf$$

in which f is the frequency of the e-m radiation and h is a constant called the **Planck constant**. By experiment, $h = 6.63 \times 10^{-34}$ Js.

Using $c = f\lambda$ (in which $c = 3.00 \times 10^8$ m s^{-1}) we can express the photon energy in terms of the wavelength of the radiation:

$$E_{phot} = \frac{hc}{\lambda}$$

Example 1

The energy of a photon (one of a pair arising from the annihilation of an electron and a positron) is 8.19×10^{-14} J. What wavelength of radiation does this represent?

Answer

Re-arranging the second equation and putting in values:

$$\lambda = \frac{hc}{E_{phot}} = \frac{6.63 \times 10^{-34} \text{ Js} \times 3.00 \times 10^8 \text{ ms}^{-1}}{8.19 \times 10^{-14} \text{ J}} = 2.43 \times 10^{-12} \text{ m}$$

This is in the γ-ray region of the e-m spectrum; note that the wavelength of visible light is about 200 000 times greater!

Example 2

A light-emitting diode produces 0.70 W of light of mean wavelength 630 nm. How many photons does it emit per second?

Answer

$$E_{phot} = \frac{hc}{\lambda} = \frac{6.63 \times 10^{-34} \text{ Js} \times 3.00 \times 10^8 \text{ ms}^{-1}}{630 \times 10^{-9} \text{ m}} = 3.16 \times 10^{-19} \text{ J}$$

$$\frac{\text{number of photons}}{\text{per second}} = \frac{\text{energy per second}}{\text{energy of 1 photon}} = \frac{0.70 \text{ Js}^{-1}}{3.16 \times 10^{-19} \text{ J}} = 2.2 \times 10^{18} \text{ s}^{-1}.$$

Some of the most direct evidence for photons comes from . . .

Key Terms

Photon = a discrete packet of electromagnetic (e-m) radiation energy.

Planck constant = h = 6.63×10^{-34} Js

》 Pointer

'Quanta' is a plural word. Its singular form is 'quantum'.

》 Pointer

For Example 1, did you check where 2.43×10^{-12} m fits on the chart of the e-m spectrum in the *Waves* section? It wouldn't be wrong to say it's in the X-ray region, but it's usually classified as γ.

quickfire

27 Calculate the energy of a photon of ultraviolet radiation of wavelength 100 nm.

quickfire

(28) Electrons are liberated from the caesium surface by yellow, green or blue light. What can be said about their photon energies, compared with those of red light?

» Pointer

The demonstration works even with no battery (the circuit being completed with a wire). Some emitted electrons reach the collecting electrode anyway.

» Pointer

Don't confuse the work function of a surface with the ionisation energy of an atom.

quickfire

(29) Calculate the maximum KE of electrons ejected from a sodium surface (see example) by light of λ = 450 nm.

The photoelectric effect

When electromagnetic radiation of high enough frequency falls on a metal surface, electrons are emitted from the surface.

For most metals, ultraviolet radiation is needed. For caesium, visible light (but not far red) will release electrons.

Demonstrating the photoelectric effect

If you've seen the (rather striking) demonstration using a metal plate attached to a gold-leaf electroscope, check that you can recall the procedure. Here is an alternative demonstration using a vacuum photocell (see diagram).

When light (of any colour but red) falls on the caesium surface, the very sensitive (nano-) ammeter registers a current.

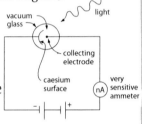

Electrons emitted from the surface into the vacuum are attracted to the collecting electrode (made positive by the battery). The electrons flow through the ammeter and the battery back to the caesium surface.

Work function of a metal surface

Although the free electrons in a metal have no ties to particular atoms, there are forces holding them to the lattice of atoms (strictly, ions) as a whole. To escape from the metal an electron has to do work against these forces. Some electrons have to do less work than others, but there is a certain minimum amount.

The **work function**, ϕ, of a metal is the minimum energy needed by an electron in order to escape from the surface.

Einstein's photoelectric equation

The key idea is that any electron that leaves the surface is ejected by a single photon. Photons don't co-operate in the ejection.

Suppose a photon gives its energy, hf, to an electron, which is able to escape. The minimum energy used in escaping is ϕ, so the maximum kinetic energy, $E_{k\,max}$, the escaped electron can have is what's left over of the photon's energy. In other words:

$$E_{k\,max} = hf - \phi$$

Example

Light of frequency 6.25×10^{14} Hz liberates electrons with a maximum kinetic energy of 4.94×10^{-20} J from a sodium surface. Calculate the work function of sodium.

Answer

$$\phi = hf - E_{k\,max} = (6.63 \times 10^{-34}\,\text{Js} \times 6.25 \times 10^{14}\,\text{s}^{-1}) - 4.94 \times 10^{-20}\,\text{J} = 3.65 \times 10^{-19}\,\text{J}$$

Minimum photon energy to release electrons

For *any* electrons to be ejected the photon energy, hf, must at the very least be equal to the work function, ϕ. We write

$$hf_{thresh} = \phi \qquad \text{that is} \qquad f_{thresh} = \frac{\phi}{h}$$

The **photoelectric threshold frequency,** f_{thresh}, of a metal, is the minimum frequency of e-m radiation needed to release an electron.

Measuring $E_{k\,max}$

We increase the pd between the caesium surface and the collecting electrode, until the current drops to zero.

At this point, the pd is called the stopping voltage, V_{stop}, because it stops all emitted electrons, even those with the most KE, from reaching the collecting electrode.

The maximum kinetic energy of the emitted electrons is given by

$$E_{k\,max} = eV_{stop}$$

e is the electronic charge.

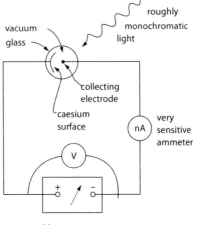

(The equation follows from the principle of conservation of energy. When electrons with greatest KE don't *quite* reach the collecting electrode they gain electrical PE of eV_{stop}.)

Experimental test of Einstein's photoelectric equation

We find $E_{k\,max}$, as just described, for three or four known frequencies, f, of light. Each could come from a (low power) laser. The wavelength could be measured with a diffraction grating, and the frequency calculated using $f = c/\lambda$.

We plot $E_{k\,max}$ against f. By comparing Einstein's equation with $y = mx + c$, we expect a straight line with a (negative) intercept equal to $-\phi$ on the vertical axis, and a positive gradient equal to h.

$$E_{k\,max} = h\,f + (-\phi)$$
$$y = m\,x + c$$

quickpire

30 The work function of sodium is 3.65×10^{-19} J. Find the threshold frequency for sodium.

Grade boost

Make sure you can draw the circuit for measuring $E_{k\,max}$. Get the polarity of the power supply correct, making the collecting electrode negative!

quickpire

31 If the stopping voltage for electrons emitted from a surface is 0.388 V, calculate $E_{k\,max}$.

quickpire

32 Why don't we use white light in testing Einstein's equation?

㉝ Find from the graph:

- The photoelectric threshold frequency for caesium.

- The work function of caesium.

- A value for the Planck constant.

㉞ An alternative graph to plot is stopping voltage, V_{stop}, against frequency, f. The gradient of this graph is h/e. What is the intercept?

㉟
- 0.010 W of light of wavelength 450 nm falls on a metal surface. How many photons arrive at it per second?

- If all the emitted electrons are collected, they make up a current of 1.5 μA. How many are emitted per second?

- What percentage of the incident photons release an electron?

The graph below uses data obtained with caesium as the emitting surface. See how you get on with Quickfires 33 and 34

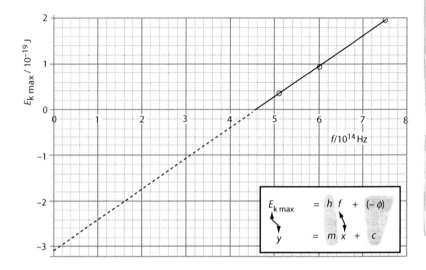

Effect of light intensity on emitted electrons

The intensity of light on a surface is the energy of electromagnetic radiation that falls per m², per second on that surface.

Suppose we increase the intensity of light on an emitting surface, without changing the frequency of the light. This will increase the number of photons falling per second on the surface, but won't affect the individual photons. We can therefore predict that:

- More photons arriving per second will eject more electrons per second. This shows up as an increase in the current, which can be confirmed using the vacuum photocell in the circuit given earlier for demonstrating the photoelectric effect.

- $E_{k\,max}$ is unaltered. Recall that photons don't co-operate in ejecting electrons. This is easily confirmed: V_{stop} is unchanged.

On a pure 'wave picture' of light, without photons, the last result can't be explained convincingly. Neither can the existence of a threshold frequency.

Atomic line emission spectra

Producing and observing the spectra

Light with a line spectrum is emitted from excited unattached atoms, for example those in the sodium vapour in a street lamp, or those which become detached from salt crystals sprinkled into a hot flame.

In the street lamp the atoms are excited (have their energy levels raised) by hits from 'missile' electrons. In the flame the atoms are excited by random hits from fast-moving molecules.

To examine the spectrum of the light emitted we use a diffraction grating. We find (repeated in each order) a **line emission spectrum** of sharp, bright, coloured lines, corresponding to (almost) single wavelengths.

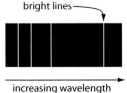

bright lines

increasing wavelength

How a line emission spectrum arises

An atom can be in various states, with different electron energy levels (See *The particle nature of matter*). The diagram below is for a hydrogen atom.

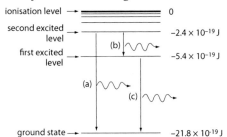

ionisation level → 0

second excited level → -2.4×10^{-19} J

(b)

first excited level → -5.4×10^{-19} J

(a)

(c)

to the right of vertical transition arrow symbolises photon leaving

ground state → -21.8×10^{-19} J

Suppose the atom (or, if you prefer, its electron) has been excited to the second excited level. It soon returns, to the (stable) ground state, either in one transition, (a), or in two transitions, (b) and (c).

In any transition, the energy the atom loses is spontaneously emitted as a single photon. So if the atom goes between levels with energies E_U (upper) and E_L (lower),

$$hf = E_U - E_L \qquad \text{So} \qquad f = \frac{E_U - E_L}{h}.$$

For example, for the photon emitted in transition (a):

$$f = \frac{-2.4 \times 10^{-19}\ \text{J} - (-21.8 \times 10^{-19}\ \text{J})}{6.63 \times 10^{-34}\ \text{Js}} = \frac{-2.4 \times 10^{-19}\ \text{J} + 21.8 \times 10^{-19}\ \text{J}}{6.63 \times 10^{-34}\ \text{Js}}.$$

So $f = 2.92 \times 10^{15}$ Hz $\qquad$ and $\qquad \lambda = \dfrac{c}{f} = \dfrac{3.00 \times 10^8\,\text{m s}^{-1}}{2.92 \times 10^{15}\,\text{s}^{-1}} = 103\ \text{nm}$

》Pointer

Don't be put off by the negative energies in the energy level diagram. They arise simply because it's conventional to assign zero energy to the ionisation level in the hydrogen atom.

quickfire

㊱ Calculate the wavelengths emitted in transitions (b) and (c). In which regions of the e-m spectrum are these wavelengths?

Grade boost

The shorter the transition arrow the longer the photon wavelength!

quickfire

㊲ *All* transitions to the ground state in a hydrogen atom will give ultraviolet radiation. How can you be sure of this? [Build on your answer to previous Quickfire 36.]

Atomic line absorption spectra

Producing and observing the spectra

They arise when e-m radiation, with a continuous range of frequencies, is sent through an 'atmosphere' containing unattached atoms.

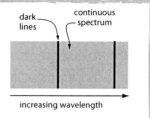

When the light that emerges is passed through a diffraction grating, dark lines are seen to cross the continuous spectrum.

The dark lines are at the exact wavelengths of some of the bright lines in the atoms' emission spectrum!

How a line absorption spectrum arises

An atom can make a transition from a lower energy level (E_L) to a higher energy (E_U) by absorbing a photon. Only a photon with energy ($E_U - E_L$) can be absorbed. A photon with a different energy will continue on its way – ignored by the atom!

In the diagram (a) and (c) represent two possible absorption events for a hydrogen atom. Event (b) won't happen at room temperature, as hardly any atoms will be at the first excited level, so they can't be promoted from it!

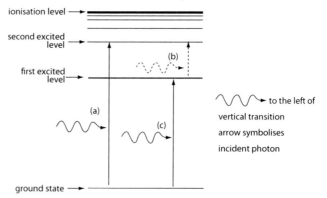

We've seen that the dark lines in the continuous spectrum correspond to absorbed photons. But won't their absorption excite the atoms, after which they will spontaneously *emit* photons of the very same frequency? Yes, but the emissions will be in random directions, so the beam of light will still lack these frequencies.

Identifying atoms from their spectra

Atoms of different elements have different energy levels, and hence different line spectra, so we can identify atoms from their spectra – even for atoms light years away! See section on stars.

Lasers

Properties and uses of laser light

A laser produces a coherent beam of light: very nearly monochromatic (single frequency), with wavefronts extending across the beam's width. This makes laser light useful for precision measurement and for carrying encoded data. Some lasers produce intense beams, useful for surgery – or welding!

LASER is an acronym for Light Amplification by Stimulated Emission of Radiation.

Stimulated emission of radiation

The diagrams symbolise three processes involving electron energy levels E_U and E_L, and photons of energy $(E_U - E_L)$. Suppose that E_L is the ground state, and E_U, the first excited level.

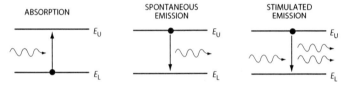

The first two processes have both been discussed.

In **stimulated emission**, a photon with energy $(E_U - E_L)$, passing near the electron at level, E_U, causes it to 'drop' to E_L, emitting a photon, of energy $(E_U - E_L)$. So we now have *two* photons of the same frequency – the beginnings of light amplification. The emitted photon is in phase with the stimulating photon, polarised in the same direction and travelling in the same direction.

Populations

For laser action ('lasing') we need this 'cloning' to happen repeatedly, creating a photon avalanche. But, without special measures, those photons that interact with electrons will be absorbed, because (at normal temperatures) almost all electrons will be in the ground state – as symbolised in the diagram below left. The ground state is *fully populated*, and the excited level is *empty*.

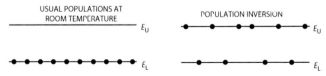

To have more stimulated emission events (each *adding* a photon) than absorption events (each *taking away* a photon) we must bring about a **population inversion**: more electrons in the excited state than the ground state. See right-hand diagram.

Key Terms

Pumping = feeding energy into the amplifying medium of a laser to produce a population inversion.

Metastable = electrons spend, on average, a long time (even milliseconds!) here before spontaneously falling.

» Pointer

Why do we need level P? If we optically pumped electrons straight from G to U then once we had as many in U as G, we'd never get in more, as we'd lose them by stimulated emission by the pumping light, as quickly as we gained them!

◉ «««« quickfire

(39) If, in a 4-level system,

$E_P = 2.7 \times 10^{-19}$ J

$E_U = 2.2 \times 10^{-19}$ J

$E_L = 0.3 \times 10^{-19}$ J

$E_G = 0$

Calculate:

(a) the wavelength of stimulated emission,

(b) the pumping energy needed per electron.

A three-level laser system

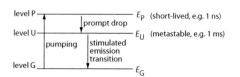

- We **pump** energy into the system to promote electrons from the ground state, G, to a 'top' level, P. One way of doing this, called optical pumping, is to shine very bright light containing photons of energy $(E_P - E_G)$ at the atoms. For the required population inversion we have to pump fast enough to keep level G less than half full.

- The system has to be chosen so that level P is very short-lived, that is electrons spend only a very short time here before making spontaneous transitions to level U. This is so that P doesn't become full, preventing further pumping.

- Level U must be **metastable**: that is electrons spend, on average, a long time (even milliseconds!) here before spontaneously falling. In this way, given a high enough pumping rate, level U can maintain a higher population than level G.

A four-level laser system

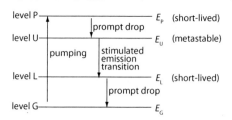

The key difference from a 3-level system is that the lower level, L, of the stimulated emission transition is *above* the ground state. This ensures that (at ordinary temperatures) it is self-emptying, by spontaneous transition to the ground state. The advantage is that we don't need such a ferocious rate of pumping (from G to P) in order to achieve population inversion between U and L, as L should always be nearly empty. (L needs to be short-lived.)

The laser itself

Photons of energy $(E_U - E_L)$ will arise by spontaneous emission within the **amplifying medium** (the material with the population inversion). Any such photon can produce a clone by stimulated emission, so 1 photon becomes 2, 2 become 4 and so on – an exponential increase. This increase is huge for photons travelling parallel to the axis of the laser and therefore likely (by repeated reflections) to traverse the medium many times, before escaping to form the beam.

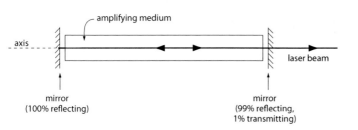

The exponential increase in photon number doesn't go on forever. It is limited by the escape of photons to form the beam, the absorption of photons, and the finite pumping rate.

Inefficiency of conventional lasers

Usually less than 1% of the pumping energy emerges in the form of laser light. Much of the pumping energy fails to raise electron levels and finishes up as random thermal energy. Even for successful pumping events, pumping energy $(E_P - E_G) > (E_U - E_L)$.

Semiconductor diode lasers

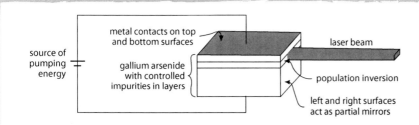

In a thin layer of material, huge population inversions can be achieved compared with those in conventional lasers, and enough amplification can be obtained with far fewer transits of photons through the amplifying medium. The 40% or so reflection that occurs naturally at the left- and right-hand faces of the population-inverted layer (see diagram) is enough; the light escaping forms the beam.

Key Term

Amplifying medium = the material with the population inversion.

≫ *Pointer*

For semiconductor lasers, you will not be asked to *draw* a diagram, nor to explain how the population inversion arises.

≫ *Pointer*

Advantages of laser diodes over other lasers include:
- Small size: chip might measure 0.5 mm × 0.5 mm × 1.0 mm.
- Far cheaper.
- Far more efficient.
- Easy to mass-produce.

≫ *Pointer*

Some uses of laser diodes include:
- Blu-ray and CD reading.
- Barcode reading.
- Data transfer (via optical fibres).
- Image scanning.
- Laser surgery.

Key Terms

Atomic number = the number of protons in its nucleus.

Mass number = the number of nucleons (number of protons + number of neutrons) in its nucleus.

Isotopes = atoms with the same number of protons, but different numbers of neutrons in their nuclei.

The particle nature of matter

Atoms

The basics

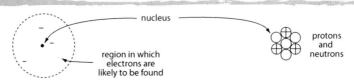

nucleus

region in which electrons are likely to be found

protons and neutrons

- Proton mass ≈ neutron mass ≈ 2000 × electron mass.
- Proton charge = $+e$, neutron charge = 0, electron charge = $-e$. ($e = 1.60 \times 10^{-19}$ C).

$_{Z}^{A}X$ Symbol for a nucleus (or atom)

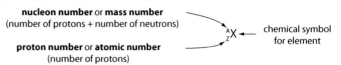

nucleon number or **mass number** (number of protons + number of neutrons)

proton number or **atomic number** (number of protons)

$_{Z}^{A}X$

chemical symbol for element

Atoms of a given element have a unique number, Z, of protons. But they can often have **isotopes**, versions of the nucleus with the same proton number but with different numbers of neutrons.

For example, hydrogen can exist as $_{1}^{1}H$ (no neutron), as $_{1}^{2}H$ (1 neutron) and as $_{1}^{3}H$ (2 neutrons).
An atom is neutral (has no resultant charge); if there are Z protons in its nucleus, there are Z electrons.

A positive **ion** is an atom which has lost an electron (or more than 1).

Atomic energy levels

We'll consider hydrogen, as it's the simplest atom, with just one electron. It can exist only in certain states, each with a definite energy. The diagram shows these energy levels.

The lower the energy of the state, the closer to the nucleus we're likely to find the electron.

The ground state is the normal state. The atom can be raised to an excited state by hitting it with missiles such as electrons.

The ionisation energy of an atom is the energy needed to remove an electron from the atom in its ground state.

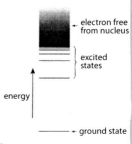

electron free from nucleus

excited states

energy

ground state

quickfire

⓵ $_{10}^{22}Ne$ and $_{11}^{23}Na$ contain equal numbers of which particle?

quickfire

㊵ Why would you expect a $_{8}^{18}O$ nucleus to have roughly 90% of the mass of a $_{10}^{20}Ne$ nucleus?

» Pointer

$_{1}^{2}H$ is sometimes called *deuterium* and $_{1}^{3}H$, *tritium*, even though they're both isotopes of hydrogen.

quickfire

㊷ A positive hydrogen ion is a hydrogen nucleus. Is it necessarily a proton?

» Pointer

The atom's energy levels are often called electron energy levels.

Quarks, leptons and generations

Protons and neutrons are, we now know, combinations of the two 'first generation' quarks, the up-quark (u) and the down-quark (d).

Charge carried by u $= +\frac{2}{3}e$.   Charge carried by d $= -\frac{1}{3}e$

The electron (e^-) is **elementary** – not some sort of combination. It is called a **lepton** ('light one') of the first generation.

There is one other first generation lepton, the electron-neutrino (v_e). This has no charge and travels at (or very close to) the speed of light. It interacts extremely rarely.

There are, in fact, three generations of particles, each with two quarks and two leptons. Ordinary matter is made from three first generation particles (u, d, e^-). We deal with first generation only.

Antiparticles

Every charged particle has an **antiparticle**, with the same mass but opposite charge. A bar over a particle's symbol denotes the antiparticle (e.g. $\bar{p}$ means an antiproton, $\bar{u}$, an anti-up-quark). An exception is the electron's antiparticle, the positron, which is denoted by e^+.

Many neutral particles have distinct antiparticles (e.g. the $\bar{n}$ is the antineutron and the $\bar{v}_e$ is the electron-antineutrino).

A particle and its antiparticle, brought together, annihilate (destroy) each other. For example:

$$e^+ + e^- \rightarrow \gamma + \gamma$$

γ denotes a gamma ray photon (see *Photons* section).

Charge conservation

Total electric charge never changes in any interaction. Note how this applies to the e^-, e^+ annihilation.

Conservation of lepton number

Each lepton is given a lepton number of 1, and each antilepton, a lepton number of -1. We find that total lepton number (for each individual generation) stays the same in any interaction.

Check how this applies to the e^-, e^+ annihilation (above). Here is another important example: the first stage in the so called p-p chain, the main process of the Sun's energy release by 'fusion'.

$$p + p \rightarrow {}^{2}_{1}H + e^+ + v_e$$

Lepton number before $= 0 + 0$. Lepton number after $= 0 + 0 + (-1) + 1$.

Grade boost

For all interactions, known or suggested, which you meet, check that charge and lepton number are conserved.

quickfire

(43) Use conservation of charge, and of lepton number, to identify particle x, in the (spontaneous) 'decay' of the neutron:

$$n \rightarrow p + e^- + x$$

quickfire

(44) Use charge and lepton conservation to identify particle y, in this (rare) interaction:

$$\bar{v}_e + p = n + y$$

Pointer

${}^{A}_{X}X$ in 'equations' for particle interactions denotes the nucleus, not the whole atom.

Baryons = combinations of 3 quarks.

Antibaryons = combinations of 3 antiquarks.

Mesons = combinations of 1 quark and 1 antiquark.

Hadrons

Protons and neutrons are but two of many particles with related properties, called hadrons. Most exist for only tiny fractions of a second. The neutron, in isolation, is 'almost stable', surviving typically for 15 minutes. The proton seems to be the only fully stable hadron.

All these hadrons are now accounted for as combinations of quarks and/or antiquarks. There are three sorts of combination ...

>> *Pointer*

Hadrons have been 'probed' by firing electrons of high KE at them. The angles and energies at which the electrons emerge give 'direct' evidence that hadrons contain more than one individual particle.

>> *Pointer*

The π^0 is a so-called linear combination of the $u\bar{u}$ and $d\bar{d}$ 'states': it could be found in either state (like Schrodinger's cat!).

Grade boost

Given that the charges of the p, n, π^+, π^- and π^0 are +e, 0, +e, –e and 0, check you can 'work backwards' to find their quark make-ups.

Baryons ('heavy ones')

Combinations of 3 quarks. The best known are the proton (uud) and the neutron (udd). Note how the quark *charges* add up correctly, e.g for the proton:

$$\frac{2}{3}e + \frac{2}{3}e + \left(-\frac{1}{3}e\right) = e.$$

Antibaryons

Combinations of 3 antiquarks. For example, the antiproton, $\bar{p}$, is $\bar{u}\bar{u}\bar{d}$, and the antineutron, $\bar{n}$, is $\bar{u}\bar{d}\bar{d}$.

Mesons ('middle ones')

Combinations of 1 quark and 1 antiquark.

The mesons which contain only first generation quarks and antiquarks are called pions (or π mesons). There are three of them:

The π^+ is $u\bar{d}$, the π^- is $\bar{u}d$, and the π^0 (neutral pion) is $u\bar{u}$ or $d\bar{d}$. It follows (check this!) from the quark make-ups of the pions that:

- their charges are $+e$, $-e$ and 0.
- the π^- is antiparticle to the π^+, but the π^0 is its own antiparticle (as there's no difference between $u\bar{u}$ and $\bar{u}u$ or between $d\bar{d}$ and $\bar{d}d$).

Conservation of baryon number

Each baryon is given a baryon number of 1, and each antibaryon, a baryon number of –1. Total baryon number doesn't change in any interaction.
This is equivalent to conservation of *total* quark number (counting antiquarks as –1).

The four fundamental forces (fundamental interactions)

The gravitational force

This acts between all bodies, even those very distant from each other. We say that the 'range' is infinite. The gravitational force is large between bodies of large mass (for example Earth and Moon) but the gravitational force between individual leptons or quarks is negligible.

The strong force

This is a force between quarks. It is not 'felt' by leptons.

The strong force holds quarks together as hadrons. The strength of the force doesn't decrease if the quarks' separation is increased, and this makes it impossible to isolate a single quark.

Attempts to smash hadrons apart by colliding them together at high KEs usually result in quark re-arrangement, and production of additional quarks and antiquarks, often grouped as mesons.

Example: $p + p \rightarrow p + n + \pi^+$.

Total u-quark number (counting a $\bar{u}$ as -1) and total d-quark number (counting a $\bar{d}$ as -1) are each conserved in a strong interaction.

Strong interactions typically occur in times of the order of 10^{-23} s.

The electromagnetic (e-m) force

This is a force of infinite range acting between electric charges.

Within the atom, e-m forces keep electrons from escaping a region surrounding the nucleus. They also bond atoms to atoms.

Absorption or emission of photons is a sign of an e-m interaction. An example is e^+, e^- annihilation:

$$e^+ + e^- \rightarrow \gamma + \gamma.$$

Total u-quark number (counting $\bar{u}$ as -1) and total d-quark number (counting $\bar{d}$ as -1) are *each* conserved in the e-m interaction.

E-m interactions typically take times of the order of 10^{-16} s.

quickfire

45. Calculate:
    (i) total u-quark number
    (ii) total d-quark number
    before and after the strong interaction,
    $$p + p \rightarrow p + n + \pi^+$$

quickfire

46. From what you know about the strong force and the e-m force, how do you know that neutrinos can't experience either?

quickfire

47. In each interaction below, work out which force is involved, giving at least two reasons:
    - $\pi^0 \rightarrow \gamma + \gamma$
      (The typical lifespan of a π^0 is 8×10^{-17} s.)
    - $\pi^+ \rightarrow e^+ + \nu_e$
      (This is one (rare) way a charged pion decays. Its typical life is 3×10^{-8} s.)
    - $\Delta^{++} \rightarrow p + \pi^+$
      (The Δ^{++} is the unstable baryon uuu. Its typical lifespan is 6×10^{-24} s.)

The weak force

This is a very short-range force experienced by both quarks and leptons. Neutrino involvement is a sign of a weak interaction.

An example is the β^- ('beta minus') decay of certain radioactive nuclei, such as $^{14}_{6}C$ (carbon 14):

$$^{14}_{6}C \rightarrow {}^{14}_{7}N + e^- + \bar{\nu}_e.$$

The nucleus has lost a neutron and gained a proton, so, leaving out those protons and neutrons which are unchanged, what happens is:

$$n \rightarrow p + e^- + \bar{\nu}_e \quad \text{that is} \quad udd \rightarrow uud + e^- + \bar{\nu}_e.$$

So a d-quark has become a u-quark – a change of quark 'flavour'!

Thus in a weak interaction involving hadrons and leptons, neither u-quark number nor d-quark number is individually conserved.

Weak interactions typically take times of the order of 10^{-8} s. Slow!

Using radiation to investigate stars

A star's spectrum

We can learn much about a star from its spectrum – how its electromagnetic (e-m) radiation energy is distributed across infrared, visible and ultraviolet wavelengths. (We find this out using a telescope, a special diffraction grating and detectors sensitive across this whole range of wavelengths.)

The spectrum consists of:

- a continuous spectrum arising from the opaque gas of the star's surface,
- a superimposed line absorption spectrum.

A star's continuous spectrum

This approximates to what physicists call a **black body** spectrum.

A black body is an ideal surface which absorbs all the e-m radiation falling on it.

Experiments show that (at any given wavelength) the best absorbers are also the best emitters. Specifically, no surface emits more radiation per m², purely because it is hot, than a black body at the same temperature.

For a black body the spectral intensity (the power emitted per m², per unit interval of wavelength) depends on the wavelength as shown in the spectra (drawn for three temperatures).

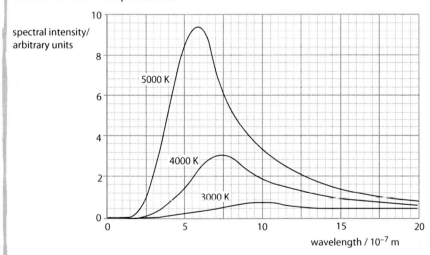

Key Term

Black body = an ideal surface which absorbs all the e-m radiation falling on it.

Grade boost

Make sure you can sketch the shape of a black body spectrum. Note the zero gradient at the origin.

quickfire

(48) In which regions of the e-m spectrum are the wavelengths of peak emission for black bodies at temperatures of:

- 5000 K?
- 4000 K?
- 3000 K?

Pointer

Don't forget that off-peak wavelengths in the visible region contribute to what we see. Suggest what colour a star at 3000 K would have.

quickfire

(49) Evaluate $T\lambda_p$ for the 3000 K, 4000 K and 5000 K spectra plotted. What does this confirm?

Intensity of e-m radiation = the power per m² of surface crossed.

Luminosity of a star = a star's e-m radiation power output.

Two laws of black body radiation

Wien's Displacement law

The wavelength, λ_p, at which the spectrum (spectral intensity plotted against wavelength) has its peak is inversely proportional to the black body's temperature.

That is
$$\lambda_P = \frac{W}{T}$$

in which W is a constant called *the Wien constant*. $W = 2.90 \times 10^{-3}$ Km.

Stefan's law (the Stefan-Boltzmann law)

The total power, P of electromagnetic radiation emitted from area A of a black body at kelvin temperature T is given by

$$P = \sigma A T^4$$

in which σ is called *the Stefan constant*. $\sigma = 5.67 \times 10^{-8}$ Wm^{-2} K^{-4}.

» **Pointer**

The relationship

Intensity $= \dfrac{P}{4\pi R^2}$

is called an inverse

square law (because if R is doubled, intensity quarters, and so on).

» **Pointer**

The inverse square law assumes no absorption of radiation by material between the star and us. In practice corrections must be made.

(50) Find the diameter of Arcturus from the calculated surface area.

Applying the black body laws to a star

Our example will be the bright red star *Arcturus*, which is known to be 3.4×10^{17} m from Earth. λ_p is measured to be 674 nm, and the intensity of radiation received on Earth from it is 3.09×10^{-8} Wm^{-2}.

- We can find the star's temperature using Wien's law:

$$\lambda_P = \frac{W}{T} \quad \text{So} \quad T = \frac{W}{\lambda_P} = \frac{2.90 \times 10^{-3} \text{ Km}}{674 \times 10^{-9} \text{ m}} = 4300 \text{ K}$$

- At the distance R of the Earth from the star, the total power, P, of e-m radiation emitted by the star is passing through a spherical surface of area $4\pi R^2$.

So the **intensity** of e-m radiation (the power per m² of surface crossed) is

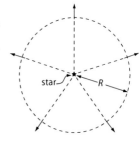

$$\text{Intensity} = \frac{P}{4\pi R^2} \quad \text{So} \quad P = \text{Intensity} \times 4\pi R^2$$

For Arcturus, $P = 3.09 \times 10^8 \text{ W} \times 4\pi (3.47 \times 10^{17} \text{ m})^2 = 4.68 \times 10^{28}$ W.

The star's e-m radiation power output is called its **luminosity**.

- Knowing a star's luminosity and its temperature, we can find its surface area, using Stefan's law. So, for Arcturus:

$$A = \frac{P}{\sigma T^4} = \frac{4.68 \times 10^{28} \text{ W}}{5.67 \times 10^{-8} \text{ Wm}^{-2}\text{K}^{-4} \times (4300 \text{ K})^4} = 2.41 \times 10^{21} \text{ m}^2$$

A star's line spectrum

This is a line absorption spectrum (revise!) arising from the passage of the continuous spectrum radiation through the star's thin atmosphere. From the wavelengths of the dark lines physicists can identify the absorbing atoms responsible for them.

We estimate from stars' spectra that, of all observable matter in the universe, about 75% by mass is hydrogen, 24% is helium and 1% or less is 'heavier' (higher Z) elements. On our current understanding, these higher Z elements weren't present in the very early universe, and those with Z > 6 are released only in extreme events like supernovae. So the Sun, which has nearly 2% by mass of higher Z elements (including oxygen, sodium, iron), must be one of a later generation of stars, which incorporate 'dust' from past supernovae. (As do we!)

Source of energy emitted from a star

A star radiates energy released in sequences of fusion reactions in its interior. For the Sun, and stars of similar mass, the commonest sequence (called the p-p1 branch of the proton-proton chain) is:

(a) $\quad {}_{1}^{1}\text{H} + {}_{1}^{1}\text{H} \quad \rightarrow \quad {}_{1}^{2}\text{H} + e^{+} + \nu_{e}$

(b) $\quad {}_{1}^{2}\text{H} + {}_{1}^{1}\text{H} \quad \rightarrow \quad {}_{2}^{3}\text{He} + \gamma$

(c) $\quad {}_{2}^{3}\text{He} + {}_{2}^{3}\text{He} \quad \rightarrow \quad {}_{2}^{4}\text{He} + {}_{1}^{1}\text{H} + {}_{1}^{1}\text{H}$

(a) is a weak interaction, and the *comparative* rarity of such events explains why the Sun's output is spread over some 10,000 million years. On the other hand, the temperature and density of its interior keeps the interaction occurring often enough for the Sun's output of e-m radiation to be 3.9×10^{26} W!

Of the neutrinos streaming out of the Sun, those coming in our direction pass through the Earth (and us), with very few interacting.

(b) and (c) involve the strong force. In (b) the e-m force also plays a part, as shown by the γ. (Its release de-excites the ${}_{2}^{3}\text{H}$ nucleus.)

The particles formed in the interactions have large kinetic energies, which are quickly randomised in collisions, making the Sun's temperature about 6000 K at its surface (and much greater inside).

Grade boost

Check that you understand, in terms of energy levels and photons, how a line absorption spectrum is produced.

Grade boost

Familiarise yourself with the steps of the p-p1 branch of the proton chain. Note that in each step the nucleus gains an extra nucleon. Starting with hydrogen (${}_{1}^{1}\text{H}$) nuclei, we finish with (${}_{2}^{4}\text{He}$) nuclei.

≫ Pointer

In the 'equations' (a), (b) and (c), we could equally well have put 'p' instead of ${}_{1}^{1}\text{H}$.

quickfire

51 Suggest what will happen to the positrons produced in step (a) of the p-p1 branch?

Summary: PH2 Waves and Particles

Waves (including Refraction)

- Longitudinal waves, transverse waves, polarisation.
- Meanings of amplitude, periodic time, frequency, in-phase oscillations, wavelength, speed of wave.
- The relationships
$f = \dfrac{1}{T}$ and $v = f\lambda$.
- Diffraction through a slit. Wavefront diagrams for the cases: slit width $> \lambda$ and slit width $\leq \lambda$.
- Waves changing media, what happens to f and λ when v changes.
- Refraction of waves: why it happens.
- Refractive index. Snell's law. $n_1 \sin\theta_1 = n_2 \sin\theta_2$.
- Critical angle and total internal reflection.
- Fibre optics, multimode dispersion, monomode fibres.
- Interference, principle of superposition, path difference rules.
- Young's 'fringes' experiment, $\lambda = \dfrac{ay}{D}$, coherence.
- The diffraction grating: comparison with Young's slits, $n\lambda = d\sin\theta$.
- Stationary (standing) waves: description in terms of amplitude and phase, nodes and antinodes, regarded as interference patterns, stationary waves on strings.
- The electromagnetic spectrum. The X-ray spectrum from an X-ray tube.
- Microwaves shown to be transverse, light shown to be transverse.

Photons

- Photons, $E_{phot} = hf$.
- The photoelectric effect, demonstrating it.
- Work function, ϕ, Einstein's equation: $E_{k\,max} = hf - \phi$, threshold frequency.
- Measuring $E_{k\,max}$, experimental test of Einstein's equation and finding a value for Planck's constant, h.
- Effect of light intensity on emitted electrons in photoelectric effect.
- Atomic line emission spectra, $hf = E_U - E_L$.
- Atomic line absorption spectra.
- Spontaneous emission, stimulated emission and absorption.
- Population of levels, population inversion.
- 3-level and 4-level laser systems.
- The laser itself, inefficiency of conventional lasers, semiconductor diode lasers.

The particle nature of matter

- Atoms: nucleus, protons, neutrons, $^A_Z X$ symbol, isotopes.
- Atomic (electron) energy levels. Ionisation and ionisation energy.
- The first generation of quarks and leptons. Antiparticles.
- Conservation of charge and lepton number.
- Hadrons: baryons and mesons.
- Strong, electromagnetic and weak interactions. Characteristic features.

Using radiation to investigate stars

- Definition of a black body, shape of black body spectrum.
- Wien's law, $\lambda_p = \dfrac{W}{T}$, using it to find temperature of a star.
- The Stefan law (the Stefan-Boltzmann law), $P = \sigma A T^4$, application to a star, for which P is called the luminosity.
- Intensity of e-m radiation. Use of $I = \dfrac{P}{4\pi R^2}$, to find luminosity P of a star.
- Origin of a star's line absorption spectrum.
- A star's energy release: the pp1 branch (3 steps) of the proton-proton fusion chain in a star such as the Sun.

Knowledge and Understanding

PH3 Practical Physics

The emphasis in the assessment PH3 is in the mastery of skills – the recall of facts and explanation of learned theory is not tested. You will need to know how to take and record measurements, to manipulate data, to investigate the relationships between variables, to estimate the uncertainty in quantities and express your results to an appropriate precision.

This unit is internally assessed. It consists of a practical exam lasting 90 minutes, with three 15-minute exercises and one 45-minute investigation. It is marked by your teacher.

Revision checklist

Tick column 1 when you have completed brief revision notes.

Tick column 2 when you think you have a good grasp of the topic.

Tick column 3 during final revision when you feel you have mastered the topic.

		1	2	3	Notes
p102	**Making and recording measurements**				
p102	Resolution				
p102	Zero error				
p103	Significant figures				
p103	**Displaying data**				
p103	Tables				
p103	Significant figures				
p104	**Graphs**				
p104	Plotting graphs				
p105	Extracting data from graphs				
p106	**Relationships between variables**				
p106	Testing relationships using raw data				
p107	Testing relationships using graphs				
p109	**Uncertainties**				
p109	Estimating uncertainty in a measurement				
p110	Percentage uncertainty				
p110	Uncertainty in derived quantities				

Key Term

Resolution (of an instrument) = the smallest measurable change it can record.

Making and recording measurements

Resolution

Record the **resolution** of the instrument you use.

Digital instrument

This is 1 in the least significant figure in the display. For example, look at the display of a multimeter set on the 200 mA range:

The resolution is 0.1 mA.

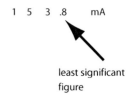

least significant figure

Analogue instrument

Take the resolution as the interval between the smallest graduations, e.g. 1 mm for a metre rule. On the voltmeter scale opposite the resolution is 0.1 V

Zero error

Always check that a measuring instrument reads 0 for a zero-sized measurement. If there is a non-zero least reading, you will need to allow for this.

Example 1
Resistance meter leads have resistance (typically around 0.4 Ω). Note the readings when the leads are touched together and subtract this from all subsequent readings on the same range.

Example 2
Micrometers usually have a zero error, which may be positive or negative. To find this, close the jaws gently and note the reading.

Example 3
The ends of metre rules are often damaged – read from the 10.0 cm mark and subtract 10.0 cm from the reading.

How many significant figures (sf) do I write down?

The general rule is to use the resolution of the instrument to the full, e.g. when using a metre rule, write down the reading to the nearest mm, e.g. 115 mm, 65.0 cm (**not** just 65 cm).

If you depart from this rule, you should draw attention to it and say why.

Example 1
You are using a −10–110°C thermometer and decide you can judge 0.5° intervals. You should be consistent, so if you are measuring to the nearest 0.5°, you should write, e.g., 35.5°C, 42.0°C.

Example 2
You are making measurements on a rapidly changing quantity, e.g. the bounce height of a ball – even if the scale is a mm scale, you might decide you can only realistically measure to the nearest cm or 5 mm.

》 Pointer
If a mass is measured to the nearest 0.1 kg and found to be 70 kg, this should be expressed as 70.0 kg. If it measured to the nearest 1 kg, the mass should be given as 70 kg (2 s.f.), in order to register the precision.

◉ ⫷⫷⫷ quickfire

① What is the resolution of a protractor?

Displaying data

Tables – marking points

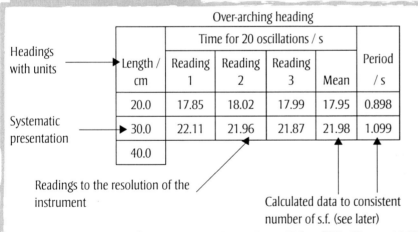

Length / cm	Time for 20 oscillations / s				Period / s
	Reading 1	Reading 2	Reading 3	Mean	
20.0	17.85	18.02	17.99	17.95	0.898
30.0	22.11	21.96	21.87	21.98	1.099
40.0					

Over-arching heading

Headings with units → Length / cm

Systematic presentation → 30.0

Readings to the resolution of the instrument

Calculated data to consistent number of s.f. (see later)

Significant figures

This is slightly tricky because there are several factors to consider when deciding how many figures to claim in a quantity you write down. If you have an uncertainty estimate, then use that as the evidence – see page 109. If not, use the figures in the data.

When multiplying and dividing, express the result to the same number of s.f. as in the least precise of the numbers used in the calculation.

quickfire

② An ohm-meter leads have a resistance of 0.3 Ω. The reading with a length of wire is 17.6 Ω. What is the wire's resistance?

quickfire

③ What should the student have written?

(a) 'The length of the A4 paper sheet = 30 cm' (measured using a metre rule)

(b) 'Current = 7.5' (measured using a digital ammeter on mA scale, resolution 0.1 mA)

(c) 'Mean value of resistance = 6.425 Ω' (Calculated from values 6.3, 6.5, 6.4 , 6.5 Ω).

Example
A piece of aluminium sheet has dimensions 1.2 mm × 5.65 cm × 2.3 cm. Calculate the volume.

Answer
If we work in cm: volume = $0.12 \times 5.65 \times 2.3 = 1.5594$ cm^3. Two of the pieces of data have only 2 significant figures, so we express the answer as 1.6 cm^3.

If we worked in mm: volume = $1.2 \times 56.5 \times 23 = 1559.4$ mm^3, which we express as 1600 mm^3 (2.s.f.)

Less commonly, we sometimes need to add or subtract data. In this case, we need to be careful of the number of decimal places in the answer.

Example
Calculate the total mass of 3 people whose individual masses are 67 kg, 58.6 kg and 70 kg.

Answer
Adding the numbers together gives 195.6 kg. If we assume that the 70 kg figure was given to the nearest kg, then the answer for the total mass should be given as 196 kg.

Graphs

Plotting graphs

Your graphs from data in PH3 will be assessed as follows:

1. **Axes** – clearly labelled to show the quantity that is being plotted. This could be an algebraic symbol, e.g. V, which should be defined.
2. **Scales** – linear (i.e. equal intervals on the scale represent equal increments in the quantity) and chosen so that the plotted points occupy at least half of the grid in both the horizontal and vertical directions. Avoid awkward intervals – with a factor of 3 or 7. It is not always necessary to include 0.
3. **Units** – with the axis labels, e.g. time / s; P / mW; acceleration / m s^{-2}.

The following plot illustrates these points: How many mistakes can you see?

- The vertical axis is not clearly labelled. Even if we assume that 'Temp' stands for temperature, the unit is not given.

- The horizontal axis is not labelled, though there is a unit (seconds) so presumably it stands for time.

- The horizontal scale is not uniform. The gap between 0 and 20 is the same as that between 20 and 30.
- The vertical scale contains an awkward factor of 3.
- The plotted points occupy less than half the vertical extent of the grid.

To see the effects of these mistakes, look at point **A** on the grid. What values does it represent?

4. **Plotting points**. Plot accurately. The maximum tolerance which is allowed is ± ½ a minor scale division.

5. **Drawing the graph**. In physics experiments, it is generally the rule that the two variables have a simple monotonic relationship (i.e. as one variable increases, the second variable either always increases or always decreases) without any sudden kinks. Because of this, a best-fit line should be drawn. Note that 'best-fit line' isn't always a straight line.

Tip for drawing a best-fit straight line

Mark in the centroid of the data points – this is the point with the mean x value, $\bar{x}$, and mean y value, $\bar{y}$. If all the points are equally uncertain, the best fit line should pass through their centroid $(\bar{x},\bar{y})$. Rotate the ruler about this point so that its edge passes as close as possible to all the points.

Extracting data from graphs

Reading off a pair of values

Drawing a best-fit line is equivalent to producing a running average of the readings. If asked to state a y-value for a given x-value, or *vice versa*, **always** take a reading from the graph, even if the given value is one of the data points – the best-fit line may not pass through the data point.

>> *Pointer*

Feel free to turn the grid on its side if that makes better use of the whole grid.

Grade boost

In timing experiments, convert minutes and seconds into seconds (e.g. 2 min 30 s = 150 s). Data in seconds are easier to plot. Also, plotting 2 min 30 s as 230 seconds by mistake happens and ruins otherwise good answers!

Finding the gradient and intercept

The gradient, m, is defined by:

$$m = \frac{\Delta y}{\Delta x}$$

On a **linear** graph, draw a large triangle, as shown, measure Δy and Δx and calculate m. Remember to think about the scale; here, 1 cm on the horizontal axis represents 10 mm.

The intercept is the reading on the vertical (y) axis where the graph hits the axis, represented by c on the graph.

If the graph is a curve, to measure the gradient at a point, draw a tangent at that point and measure the gradient, as for a linear graph.

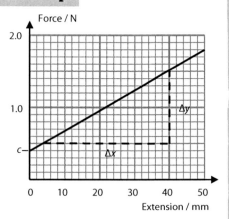

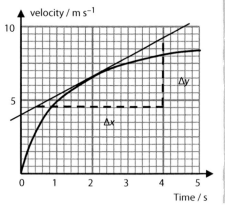

Relationships between variables

Testing relationships using raw data

You can use data from experiments to test whether two variables are:

- proportional (or 'directly proportional')
- linearly related
- inversely proportional.

The variables are identified as x and y below.

(a) **Proportional**: variable y is (directly) proportional to x – or x and y are (directly) proportional – if $\frac{y}{x} = k$, where k is a constant. This relationship can be written:

$$y \propto x$$

(b) **Linear relationship**: if y is linearly related to x, then equal increases in x produce equal increases in y.

(c) **Inversely proportional**: variable y is inversely proportional to x if $xy = k$, where k is a constant. This relationship can be written:

$$y \propto \frac{1}{x}$$

(d) **Different relationships**: we can use one of these three tests for other similar functions too, e.g. we can test whether $y \propto x^2$. Just use x^2 instead of x in the first test, ie look at the ratio $\dfrac{y}{x^2}$. If it is always the same then $y \propto x^2$.

Similarly, if $x^2 y = $ constant then $y \propto \dfrac{1}{x^2}$.

Exercise: Look at the following table of data – then do the Quickfire question.

x	Dependent variables			
	y_1	y_2	y_3	y_4
2.0	30.0	1.5	0.8	1.0
4.0	15.0	2.5	1.6	4.0
6.0	10.0	3.5	2.4	9.0
8.0	7.5	4.5	3.2	16.0

The problem with using raw data to test relationships is that experimental data are not perfect. This means that multiplying pairs of values of the two variables does not always give exactly the same answer, even if the two variables are inversely proportional.

Grade boost

If y is halved when x is doubled, then $y \propto \dfrac{1}{x}$.

quickfire

⑥ What can you say about the relationship between each of the variables y_1, y_2, y_3, and y_4 and the independent variable x?

Testing relationships using graphs

This is a much more powerful tool than using raw data.

The relationship between two variables is linear if a graph of y against x is a straight line.

The variables are related by the equation:

$$y = mx + c$$

where c is the intercept on the y axis and m is the gradient defined by:

$$m = \frac{\Delta y}{\Delta x}.$$

If $y \propto x$, the graph is a straight line also but the intercept, c, is 0.

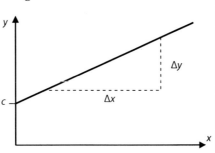

Grade boost

The gradient is the term that multiplies the variable on the right-hand side of the equation.

For a constant acceleration, $v = u + at$. From a graph of v against t, the intercept is u and the gradient is a.

⑦ The diffraction grating equation can be written $d \sin \theta = n\lambda$. If $\sin \theta$ is plotted against n, what are the gradient and intercept? How can λ be found?

⑧ (a) What is the gradient of a graph of T^2 against m?

(b) What other graph would be a straight line and how would you find k from it?

⑨ The relationship between the pd, V, across a power supply and the external resistance, R, can be written:

$$\frac{1}{V} = \frac{r}{ER} + \frac{1}{E}.$$

(a) What graph, with V and R as variables, would be a straight line?

(b) How would you use it to find E and r?

Example

The relationship between the terminal pd, V, and the current, I, through a power supply is:

$$V = E - Ir,$$

where E is the emf and r the internal resistance. If E and r are constant the relationship between V and I is linear and we can use a graph of V against I to determine the emf and internal resistance.

Re-writing the equation for the cell: $V = (-r) I + (E)$

Comparing with the linear equation: $y = (m) x + (c)$

The double arrows indicate that, if we plot a graph of V (y-axis) against I (x-axis), it should be a straight line with intercept E on the V axis and gradient $-r$.

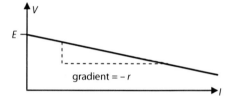

gradient $= -r$

If the relationship between the variables is not linear

Think about the equation for constant acceleration $v^2 = u^2 + 2ax$, with v and x the variables. This is not a linear equation because v is squared, so a plot of v against x would not be a straight line. If we plot v^2 against x, this is what happens

Re-arranging the equation: $v^2 = (2a) x + (u^2)$

Comparing with the linear equation: $y = (m) x + (c)$

The graph should be a straight line with gradient $2a$ and intercept u^2 on the v^2 axis – so we can easily find a and u from the graph.

Another example (you will meet this in PH4). The period T of oscillation on a mass m on a spring is given by:

$$T = 2\pi\sqrt{\frac{m}{k}},$$ where k is the spring constant.

Now look at Quickfire 8.

Uncertainties

No measurements, apart from guaranteed whole numbers (e.g. the number of students in a lab) are 100% accurate. You should be aware of and, if possible, estimate, the uncertainties in all quantities you obtain through experiment. The scientific estimation of uncertainties involves probabilities but in the WJEC A level course, the approach is simpler:

We express a result, e.g. a density determination, with its uncertainty as follows: Density, $\rho = 2300 \pm 100$ kg m^{-3}. The 100 kg m^{-3} is the uncertainty – strictly the 'absolute uncertainty' (see below). This means that the best estimate of the density is 2300 kg m^{-3} but that its value could lie between 2200 and 2400 kg m^{-3}.

Estimating the absolute uncertainty in a measurement

If we only have a single measurement

The instrument resolution should be used as the uncertainty in the measurement, e.g. when measuring lengths using a metre rule, the uncertainty should be given as 0.001 m.

If we have several measurements, i.e. repeats

Suppose we make several measurements of the bounce height of a ball when dropped from 1.000 m. The readings are: 0.785 m, 0.780 m, 0.784 m, 0.787 m, 0.783 m. What bounce height do we report?

Bounce height

$$= \text{mean value} \pm \frac{\text{maximum value} - \text{minimum value}}{2} \text{ (i.e. mean} \pm \text{½ the spread)}$$

$$= 0.7838 \pm \frac{0.787 - 0.780}{2} \text{m}$$

$$= 0.7838 \pm 0.0035 \text{ m}$$

Rule 1: give the uncertainty estimate to 1 significant figure, i.e. 0.004 m in this case.

Rule 2: give the best estimate to the same number of decimal places as the estimate of the absolute uncertainty.

So, applying both these rules: Bounce height = 0.734 ± 0.004 m, which means, 'the best estimate of the bounce height is 0.734 m but it could be anywhere in a range of 0.004 m either side of this figure'.

>> Pointer

The uncertainty can be expressed to 2 s.f. if the first significant figure is 1, e.g. a resistance expressed as 5.25 ± 0.13 Ω is acceptable.

Grade boost

The percentage uncertainty in $\sqrt{x}$ is ½ × the percentage uncertainty in x. Similarly $p(\sqrt[3]{x}) = \frac{1}{3}p(x)$

Grade boost

In the sphere formula, $V = \frac{4}{3}\pi r^3$, the values of $\frac{4}{3}$ and π are exact, i.e. they have zero uncertainty, so the percentage uncertainty in $V = 3 \times$ the percentage uncertainty in r.

quickpire

⑩ How should you express the pressure of a car tyre from the following measurements:

225 kPa, 229 kPa, 219 kPa and 213 kPa?

Grade boost

If a diameter, d, is measured and used to calculate the radius, r, then $p(r) = p(d)$.

Percentage uncertainty

When we combine quantities by multiplying and dividing, we need to consider the percentage uncertainty, p. This is defined by:

$$p = \frac{\text{absolute uncertainty}}{\text{best estimate}} \times 100\%$$

e.g. The emf of a cell is 1.57 ± 0.04 V. The percentage uncertainty $p = \frac{0.04}{1.57} \times 100\% = 2.55\%$. Again this is normally expressed to 1 s.f. (3 %) but you should keep more s.f. in the middle of calculations.

Uncertainties in derived quantities

Most equations in physics require quantities to be multiplied together or for one quantity to be divided by another.

Examples: $R = \dfrac{V}{I}$; $E_p = mgh$.

When we combine quantities in these ways, the percentage uncertainty in the result is the sum of the percentage uncertainties in the quantities, e.g. using the first example above $p_R = p_V + p_I$ (Note: here p_R means the percentage uncertainty in R, etc.)

Example

The percentage uncertainties in V and I are 2% and 3% respectively. The calculated value of the resistance is 539.2 Ω. How should this be expressed?

Answer

Adding the ps: $p_R = 2\% + 3\% = 5\%$.

The absolute uncertainty in R is $5\% \times 539.2\ \Omega = 30\ \Omega$ (to 1 s.f.), so the resistance should be expressed as $540 \pm 30\ \Omega$.

Sometimes we need raise a quantity to a power, e.g. Volume $= \dfrac{4}{3}\pi r^3$. The quantity r^3 is just $r \times r \times r$ so, using the above rule, the percentage uncertainty in r^3, p_{r^3} is $3 \times$ the percentage uncertainty in r. The general rule is $p_{x^n} = n \times p_x$.

quickfire

⑪ An asteroid's speed is given as 35.2 ± 0.5 km s^{-1}. What is the percentage uncertainty?

quickfire

⑫ The volume of a cylinder is given by $V = \pi r^2 l$.
   (a) If $p_r = 0.5$ % and $p_l = 0.8$ %, what is p_V?
   (b) If the calculated value of V is 15.34 cm^3, how should the volume be expressed?

quickfire

⑬ A ball bearing has a diameter of 1.00 ± 0.01 cm. What is its volume?

Practice questions

Definition-type questions

1. A body is acted on by a number of forces. State the conditions needed for the body to be in equilibrium.
   [Basic physics – PH1.1]

2. In terms of electromagnetic radiation, a star can be considered as a *black body*.
   What is meant by the term 'black body'?
   [Using radiation to investigate stars – PH2.4]

3. Progressive waves can be either *transverse* or *longitudinal*.
   Distinguish between transverse and longitudinal waves and give an example of each.
   [Waves – PH2.1]

4. 'The potential difference across a component is 5.0 V.'
   Explain this statement in terms of energy.
   [Resistance – PH1.5]

5. State Ohm's Law.
   [Resistance – PH1.5]

6. State the meaning of the term 'transition temperature' when applied to electrical conductors.
   [Resistance – PH1.5]

7. State the Principle of Superposition.
   [Waves – PH2.1]

8. *Hadrons* are composite particles, which are classified as either *baryons* or *mesons*.
   State what is meant by each of the terms in italics and give an example of a baryon and a meson.
   [Matter, force and the universe – PH2.3]

9. If data are transmitted over long distances through multimode fibres, different pieces of data can be received at the same time.
   State the name for the cause of this problem.
   [Refraction of light – PH2.1]

10. An electrical power supply has an *EMF of 10.0 V* and the *pd across its terminals is 9.0 V*.
    Explain the expressions in italics in terms of energy.
    [DC circuits – PH1.6]

Experimental description questions

11. (a) Starting from a defining equation, show that the unit of resistivity is Ω m.

    (b) Describe an experiment to determine the resistivity of a metal in the form of a metal wire.

    [Resistance – PH1.5]

12. Describe an experiment to investigate how the resistance of a metal wire varies with temperature.

    [Resistance – PH1.5]

    Sketch a graph to show the expected variation.

13. The diagram shows a circuit containing a vacuum photocell. The metal surface in the photocell is irradiated with electromagnetic radiation of fixed frequency.

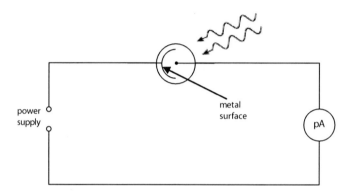

(a) Describe how you can determine the maximum kinetic energy of the photoelectrons. You should add any necessary labels and components to the diagram.

(b) In a further experiment, the maximum kinetic energy of the emitted electrons is measured for a range of frequencies of incident radiation. A graph of the results is as follows:

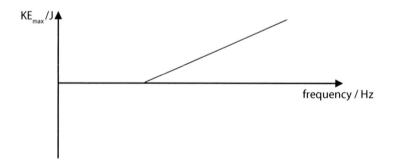

From the graph, state how you would determine:

 (i) the Planck constant;

(ii) the work function of the metal.

[Photons – PH2.2]

Questions to test understanding

14. It is suggested that the speed, v, of transverse waves on a stretched string is related to the tension, T, and the mass per unit length, μ, of the string, by the equation

$$v = k\sqrt{\frac{T}{\mu}},$$

where k is a dimensionless constant. Show that this is possible.

[Basic Physics – PH1.1]

15. The graph shown is of a skydiver who reaches terminal velocity then opens the parachute.

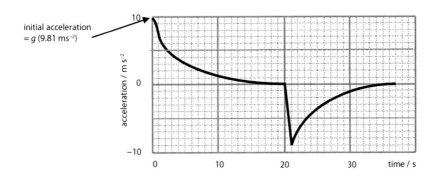

(a) Explain why the acceleration changes direction and then decreases to zero.

(b) Explain why the area between the line and the x-axis must be overall positive.

[Kinematics – PH1.2]

16. Three resistors are connected in a network as shown.

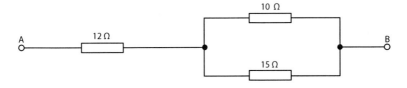

A power supply of EMF 9.0 V and negligible internal resistance is connected between A and B. Calculate the pd across the 12 Ω resistor.

[DC circuits – PH1.6]

17. A cell has EMF 1.5 V and internal resistance 0.5 Ω. It is connected across a 12.5 Ω resistor.

(a) Calculate the current in the circuit.

(b) A number of identical such cells are to be connected in series across the same resistor in order that the current is at least 0.60 A.

Calculate the minimum number of cells required.

[DC circuits – PH1.6]

18. A skydiver falling through the air experiences a drag force which is directly proportional to the square of her velocity.

$$F = k\,v^2.$$

(a) Show that a suitable unit for k is $N\,m^{-2}\,s^2$ and express this unit in terms of the base SI units, m, kg and s, only.

(b) A skydiver has a mass of 75 kg. The value of k for her is $0.30\,N\,m^{-2}\,s^2$.

   (i) Calculate the resultant force on the skydiver when she is falling at a velocity of $20\,m\,s^{-1}$.

   (ii) Show that her terminal velocity is approximately $50\,m\,s^{-1}$.

   (iii) Estimate the time it takes her to accelerate from $35\,m\,s^{-1}$ to $45\,m\,s^{-1}$. Explain your working clearly.

[Kinematics – PH1.2]

19. The diagram shows a potential divider used as a power supply.

Show that $\dfrac{V_{OUT}}{V_{IN}} = \dfrac{R}{R + X}$:

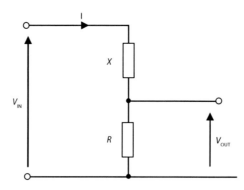

[DC circuits – PH1.6]

20. In the following circuit the lamps, L_1, L_2 and L_3, are identical. The switch, S, is closed and all lamps are on. You may assume that the switch has negligible resistance.

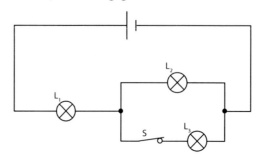

(a) Compare the brightness of the 3 lamps, L_1, L_2 and L_3.
   Explain your answer.

(b) Switch S is now opened so lamp L_3 is off. State what effect this has on the brightness of L_1 and L_2 and explain your answer.

[DC circuits – PH1.6]

PH3 Practical Physics questions

21. You are given a ream of A4 paper [500 sheets] and a 30 cm rule. By taking suitable measurements, calculate the volume of a single sheet of paper. Give the uncertainty in the volume and express your answers to an appropriate number of significant figures.

    Results

    Thickness of 500 sheets of paper tightly held = 5.15 cm

22. This circuit has been set up for you.

    Theory predicts that the current, I, is related to the external resistance, R, by the equation.

    $$\frac{1}{I} = \frac{R}{E} + \frac{r}{E}$$

    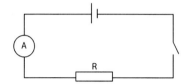

    where E is the EMF of the cell and r the internal resistance.

    You are provided with a set of resistors.

    (a) By inserting them into the circuit in turn, take a series of measurements of current. Record your measurements in the table.

    (b) Complete the table.

    (c) Plot a graph of $1/I$ on the vertical axis against R on the horizontal axis.

    (d) Comment on how well the graph supports the theoretical equation.

    (e) By taking suitable measurements on the graph, determine the EMF and internal resistance of the cell.

R/Ω	I/A	$\dfrac{1}{I(A)}$
1.5	0.866	
2.2	0.656	
3.3	0.441	
3.8	0.388	
4.7	0.313	
5.6	0.271	

Exam Practice and Technique

Exam practice and skills

The exam papers are written by Principal Examiners well in advance of the date of the examination. A committee of experienced examiners and teachers checks and modifies the papers to ensure they have suitable content and wording.

Exam tips

Read the question carefully. Examiners discuss the wording of questions so that the meaning is clear and precise. It is easy to misinterpret a question, so take your time. Using a highlighter to mark key information often helps, e.g. numerical information given at the beginning of a question is sometimes not needed until later on, so highlighting this makes it stand out.

Look at the mark allocation

Each part of a question is allocated a number of marks. In written answers, this total gives a hint as to how much detail you need in your answer. In calculations, some marks will be for the working and some for the answer (see below).

Understand the command words

These are the words which show the sort of answer which the examiner expects in order to give you credit.

State (a fact)

A short answer with no explanation.

State (a law or definition)

This requires you to recall a law or definition that you have learnt, e.g. 'State Ohm's Law'.

Explain

Give a reason or reasons. Look at the mark allocation: 2 marks usually means that you need to make two distinct points. It may be worth making an extra point 'just to be sure' but be careful you do not contradict yourself.

State ... and explain

There may be a mark for the statement but the first mark may be for an explanation of a correct statement, e.g. '*State which resistor, A or B, has the higher value and explain your reasoning.*' It is unlikely that the examiner will give you a mark for a 50/50 choice!

Calculate

A correct answer will score all the marks, unless the question includes the instruction to '*show your working*'. **Warning**: An incorrect answer without working will score 0.

Always give the units of your answer – missing or incorrect units will be penalised.

Show that (in a calculation question)

E.g. '*Show that the resistivity is approximately $2 \times 10^{-7}\ \Omega\ m$.*' There is no mark here for just the correct answer; the working must be shown in sufficient detail for the examiner to be convinced you know what you are doing! **Hint**: In this case, calculate an accurate answer, e.g. $1.85 \times 10^{-7}\ \Omega$ m and say that this is approximately the value stated.

Describe

A series of statements is required. These may be independently marked but care may be needed with sequencing, e.g. in the description of how to carry out an experiment.

Compare

There must be a clear comparison, not just two separate statements. It is also not safe just to state one thing and leave the examiner to infer another; e.g. '*Compare the work functions of metals A and B.*'

Answer 1: Metal A has a low work function – not enough.

Answer 2: Metal A has a lower work function **than metal B** – this answer would gain credit (if correct!) unless the question makes it clear that a numerical comparison is required.

Suggest

This command word often comes at the end of a question. You are expected to put forward a sensible idea based upon your physics knowledge and the information in the question. There will often be more than one correct answer.

Name

A single word or phrase is expected; e.g. *'Name the property of light being demonstrated'* (in a question showing waves spreading out after passing through a gap). Answer: *Diffraction*. Note that, especially in this kind of question, a correctly spelt answer may be required.

Estimate

This does not mean 'guess'. It usually involves one or more calculations with simplifying assumptions. The question may ask you to state any assumptions you make. E.g. *'Estimate the number of 1 mm diameter spheres which will fill a measuring cylinder up to the 100 cm³ mark.'*

Derive

This involves producing this equation starting from a set of assumptions and/or more basic equations. You should learn the derivations of these equations:

$$v = u + at, \quad x = ut + \tfrac{1}{2} at^2, \quad I = nAve,$$

$$E_{\text{elastic}} = \tfrac{1}{2} kx^2 \text{ and } \frac{V_{\text{OUT}}}{V_{\text{IN}}} = \frac{R}{R_{\text{total}}}$$

Tips about diagrams

Questions about experiments sometimes ask for diagrams. The diagram should show the arrangement of the apparatus and be labelled. Separate diagrams of a metre rule, a length of wire, a micrometer and an ohm-meter, will gain no credit. Note, however, that standard circuit symbols, e.g. a cell or a voltmeter, do not need labelling. Even if the question does not demand one, some of the marks may be awarded for information included in a well-drawn diagram.

Tips about graphs

Graphs from data: where the axes and scales are not drawn, make sure that you choose the scale so that the points occupy at least half of the given grid (on theory papers, the examiners usually choose a grid size which makes this easy). Label the axes with the name, or symbol, of the variable with its unit – e.g. time / s, or F / N – and include scales. Plot points as accurately as possible; for points requiring interpolation between grid lines, the usual tolerance is ± ½ a square. Unless the question instructs differently, draw in the graph.

Sketch graphs (in PH1 and PH2 papers): a sketch graph gives a good idea of the relationship between the two variables. It needs labelled axes but often it will not have scales and units. It is **not** an untidy ('hairy') graph. If the graph is intended to be a straight line, it should be drawn using a ruler. Sometimes significant values need to be labelled.

Tips about calculations

1. If the command word is **calculate** or **find** or **determine**:

   Full marks are given for the correct answer **but** an incorrect answer with no working scores 0 and there are usually marks available for correct steps in the working, even if the final answer is incorrect. Points the examiner will look for will include:

   - Selection of equation or equations and writing them down.
   - Conversion of units, e.g. hours into seconds, mA into A.
   - Insertion of values into equation(s) and manipulation of equation.
   - Stating the answer – **remember the unit**.

   Example: *A piece of wire of length 5.0 m has a diameter of 1.0 mm. The resistivity of the material is 4.7 × 10⁻⁷ Ω m.*

   Calculate the resistance of the wire.   [3]

   Working: Equations: $R = \dfrac{\rho l}{A}$ $A = \pi r^2$

   Resistance $= \dfrac{4.7 \times 10^{-7} \times 5.0}{\pi \times (0.5 \times 10^{-3})^2}$ ✓✓

   (1 mark for correct use of equations; 1 for conversion of diameter to radius)

So resistance $= 3.0\ \Omega$ ✓ (1 mark for correct answer with unit).

2. If the command phrase is **show that**, the basic rules for the setting out are the same. You **must** give clear convincing steps.

Example: *A model rocket ascends vertically. At a height of 100 m and travelling upwards at 60 m s^{-1}, its fuel runs out. Show that the maximum height it reaches is approximately 300 m. (Ignore air resistance).* [3]

Working: (Note that there is more than one way of tackling this question. This solution uses energy conversion.)

At 100 m the total energy [kinetic + potential] of the rocket

$$= \tfrac{1}{2}\,mv^2 + mg \times 100 ✓$$

$$= m\,[1800 + 981]$$

$$= 2781\,m$$

At the highest point, height h, KE $= 0$

∴ Total energy $= mgh = 9.81\,mh$

∴ By the Principle of Conservation of Energy, $9.81\,mh = 2781\,m$ ✓

Dividing by m and rearranging:

$$h = \frac{2781}{9.81} = 283\ \text{m} \approx 300\ \text{m} ✓$$

(1 mark for applying correct principles; 1 for making allowance of the 'initial' height of 100 m; one mark for convincing algebra/manipulation.)

Tips about describing experiments

Several statements in both the PH1 and PH2 sections of the specification require knowledge of experimental procedure, e.g. determining the resistivity of the material of a wire or measuring the maximum KE of photo-electrons.

- Draw a simple diagram of the apparatus (see Tips about diagrams).
- Give a clear list of steps.
- Say what measurements are made and which instrument will be used.
- Say how the final determination will be made from your measurements.

Tips about questions involving units

This is mainly dealt with in the section PH1 – Units and Dimensions. One type of question requires you to suggest a unit for a quantity.

The question will always give an equation involving the quantity.

- Manipulate the equation to make the unknown quantity the subject.
- Insert the known units for the other quantities.
- Simplify.

E.g. *The drag, **F**, on a sphere of radius **a** moving slowly with a velocity v through a fluid is given by F = 6πηav*

where η is a constant called the coefficient of viscosity. Suggest a unit for η.

Make η the subject: $\eta = \dfrac{F}{6\pi a v}$

Rewrite in terms of units:

∴ unit of $\eta = \dfrac{\text{N}}{\text{m} \times \text{m}\,\text{s}^{-1}} = \text{N m}^{-2}\,\text{s}.$

Note: The question did not ask for any particular form, e.g. reducing it to the base units, so it can be left like this. The pascal, Pa, is equivalent to N m^{-2} so another equivalent is Pa s.

Questions and answers

This part of the guide looks at actual student answers to questions. There is a selection of questions covering a wide variety of topics. In each case there are two answers given; one from a student (Seren) who achieved a high grade and one from a student who achieved a lower grade (Tom). We suggest that you compare the answers of the two candidates carefully; make sure you understand why one answer is better than the other. In this way you will improve your approach to answering questions. Examination scripts are graded on the performance of the candidate across the whole paper and not on individual questions; examiners see many examples of good answers in otherwise low scoring scripts. The moral of this is that good examination technique can boost the grades of candidates at all levels.

PH1: Motion, Energy and Charge

PH2: Waves and Particles

Q&A

1

(a) (i) Define work. [2]
(ii) Hence express the unit of work, J, in terms of the SI base units kg, m and s. [2]

(b)

A skier of mass 70 kg descends a slope as shown. The skier passes point **A** at a speed of 6 m s⁻¹ and **B** at 21 m s⁻¹. Calculate for the descent from **A** to **B**:
(i) The gravitational potential energy lost by the skier. [2]
(ii) The kinetic energy gained by the skier. [3]
(c) (i) State the principle of conservation of energy. [1]
(ii) Discuss your answer to (b) (i) and (ii) in terms of this principle. [2]
(d) Calculate the mean resistive force experienced by the skier between **A** and **B**. [4]

Seren's answer

(a) (i) The force exerted multiplied by the distance✓ travelled in the direction of the force. ✓

(ii) $[F] = N = kg\ m\ s^{-2}$
$[d] = m$ ✓
$\therefore [W] = J = [F] \times [d] = kg\ m^2\ s^{-2}$ ✓

(b) (i) $\Delta gpe = mg\Delta h$
$= 70 \times 9.81 \times (120\sin 20)$ ✓
$= 28183.82739\ J = 28.2\ kJ\ (3\ s.f.)$ ✓

(ii) $KE = \left(\frac{1}{2}mv_2^2\right) - \left(\frac{1}{2}mv_1^2\right)$ ✓
$= \left(\frac{1}{2}70 \times 21^2\right) - \left(\frac{1}{2}70 \times 6^2\right)$ ✓
$= 14175\ J = 14.2\ kJ$ ✓

(c) (i) Energy can neither be created nor destroyed, but converted into other forms of energy. ✓

(ii) The gravitational potential energy that has been lost between A and B has been converted into other forms of energy, ✓ including thermal, kinetic and sound.

(d) $Fx = \frac{1}{2}mv^2 - \frac{1}{2}mu^2$ ✓
$120\ F = \frac{1}{2}70 \times 21^2 - \frac{1}{2}70 \times 6^2$ ✗
$120\ F = 14175$ ✓
$F = 118\ N\ (3\ s.f.)$ ✗

Examiner commentary

(a) (i) Seren has correctly included the often-forgotten statement about direction.

(ii) The first mark is for correctly identifying the force and distance units and the second for the manipulation. Note: Seren has used square brackets, [. . .], to indicate 'the unit of', which is quick.

(b) (i) Seren has gained 1 mark for correct substitution and 1 mark for the answer. In this case, converting to kJ and expressing to 3 s.f. gained no extra credit.

(ii) Fully correct. Note that, if Seren had slipped up in the final calculation, she would have received 2 marks because her working was clear and correct.

(c) (i) A mark which most candidates achieve.

(ii) Seren has identified that the initial GPE was converted into several other forms [i.e. not just kinetic] but has missed out any discussion of mechanism, e.g. work done against friction/drag.

(d) Seren has used the principle: Work done = energy transfer and used it to calculate a force from the change of KE. Unfortunately, she has calculate the resultant force on the skier, not the resistive force.

Seren gains 13 out of 16 marks.

Tom's answer

(a) (i) The amount of energy used over a certain time ✗

(ii) $J = \dfrac{kg \times m}{s}$ ✗

(b) (i) $\Delta E_p = mg\Delta h \qquad\qquad 120\cos 20 = 112.76\,m$

$= 70 \times 9.81 \times 112.76$ ✓ e.c.f.

$= 77432\,J$ ✗

(ii) $KE = \dfrac{1}{2}mv^2$

$= \dfrac{1}{2}70 \times 15^2 \; 70 \times 15^2$ ✓ $= 7875\,J$ ✗

(c) (i) Energy cannot be created or destroyed, only transferred into other forms. ✓

(ii) The gravitational potential energy gained by the skier has been converted into kinetic energy. ✗

(d) $a = \dfrac{v^2 - u^2}{240} = \dfrac{21^2 - 36}{240} = 1.6875\,m\,s^{-2}$

$F = ma = -70 \times 1.6875 =$ ✓

Examiner commentary

(a) (i) Tom's definition is of power rather than work.

(ii) Tom's answer follows on from his confusion between work and power. *Error carried forward* would not be applied here, even if his working was correct for power, as it is a mistake of principle.

(b) (i) Tom has quoted the correct equation for ΔE_p and the first mark is for correctly using it. Unfortunately he has used cos 20° which gives the horizontal rather than the vertical distance so he just gets one mark for substitution.

(ii) Tom has quoted the KE formula and substituted a speed so receives 1 mark. Unfortunately he has used the speed difference for v rather than working out the two values of $\dfrac{1}{2}mv^2$ and finding the difference.

(c) (ii) Tom has not done enough for the first mark. He needed to account for the fact that gain in kinetic energy was less than the loss in gravitational potential energy.

(d) Tom has calculated the acceleration and, apart from the minus sign, has almost calculated the <u>resultant</u> force on the skier. This is the start of a possible method and has attracted 1 mark.

Tom gains 4 out of 16 marks.

(a) A velocity–time graph is given for a body which is accelerating in a straight line.

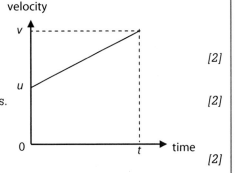

(i) Using the symbols given on the graph, write down an expression for the gradient and state what it represents. [2]

(ii) Using the symbols given on the graph, write down an expression for the area under the graph and state what it represents. [2]

(iii) Hence or otherwise show clearly that, using the usual symbols,

$$x = ut + \frac{1}{2}at^2$$ [2]

(b) A cyclist accelerates **from rest** with a constant acceleration of 0.50 m s⁻² for 12.0 s. Calculate:

(i) the distance travelled in this time [2]

(ii) the maximum velocity attained. [2]

(c) After 12.0 s, the cyclist stops pedalling and 'freewheels' to a standstill with constant deceleration over a distance of 120 m.

(i) Calculate the time taken for the cyclist to decelerate to a stand-still. [2]

(ii) Calculate the magnitude of the cyclist's deceleration. [2]

(d) Draw an acceleration–time graph on the grid for the **whole of the cyclist's journey.** [4]

(e) In reality the cyclist would not slow down with constant deceleration. This is because the total resistive force acting on the cyclist consists of a constant frictional force of 8.0 N **and** an air resistance force which is proportional to the square of the cyclist's velocity.

(i) When the cyclist was travelling with maximum velocity, the total resistive force acting was 165 N. Calculate the force of air resistance at this velocity. [1]

(ii) Hence calculate the total resistive force acting when the cyclist is moving at half the maximum velocity. [2]

Seren's answer

(a) (i) $\dfrac{v-u}{t} = a$, acceleration ✓✓

(ii) $ut + \dfrac{1}{2}(v-u)t$ ✓ = distance travelled ✓

(iii) Distance travelled, $x = ut + \dfrac{1}{2}(v-u)t$

$\dfrac{v-u}{t} = a$ so $v - u = at$ ✓

Substituting for $(v-u)$:

$x = ut + \dfrac{1}{2}att = ut + \dfrac{1}{2}at^2$ ✓

(b) (i) $ut + \dfrac{1}{2}at^2$

$0 + \dfrac{1}{2} \times 0.5 \times 144 = 36$ m ✓✓

(ii) 0.5×12 s = 6 m/s ✓✓

(c) (i) $s = \dfrac{1}{2}(u+v)t$

$t = \dfrac{120}{3} = 40$ s ✓✓

(ii) $\dfrac{6}{40} = 0.15$ m s^{-2}. ✓✓

Examiner commentary

(a) (i) Ideally Seren would have started her answer, 'Gradient =. . . .' but that is assumed by the marker and full marks awarded.

(ii) Seren gives a fully correct answer. She doesn't simplify the expression to $\dfrac{1}{2}(v+u)t$, but that is not a requirement of the question.

(iii) Seren's working is made easier by the fact that she didn't simplify the expression for **x** in part (ii)! This is a 'show that' question and Seren has explained her steps clearly.

(b) (i) As *in (a)(i)*, the '**x** =' is missing but the working is clear, concise and correct.

(ii) Unlike Tom, Seren has used the easy method here: $v = u + at$. She doesn't write the symbol equation but this doesn't matter, as the command word is 'calculate,' so a correct answer, even with no working, would be accepted. This is also the case in (c) (ii)

(d) Scales ✓, horizontal lines ✓✓, change at 12 s. ✓ Seren has incorrectly included a vertical line down to –0.5 m s^{-2} at 52 seconds but the examiner has decided to give her 'benefit of doubt' as it wasn't mentioned in the mark scheme.

(e) (i) Seren correctly subtracts 8 N to calculate the air resistance at the maximum velocity.

(ii) Seren has arrived at the correct answer and her reasoning is clear. The mathematical nonsense of $\dfrac{157}{4} = 39.25$ N + 8 N is tolerated. Better would have been:

Air resistance force at half the maximum velocity = $\dfrac{157}{4} = 39.25$ N

∴ Total resistive force = 39.25 N + 8 N = 47.25 N

Seren gains 21 out of 21 marks.

(d) acceleration (m/s²)

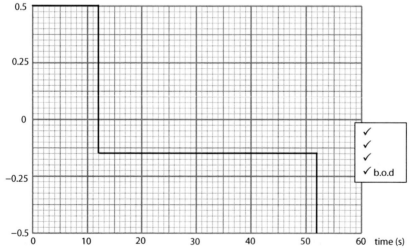

(e) (i) 157 N ✓

(ii) $157 \times 1^2 \rightarrow 157 \times 0.5^2 = \dfrac{157}{4} = 39.25$ N + 8 N = 47.25 N ✓✓ [In spite of the setting out!]

Tom's answer

(a) (i) The gradient represents acceleration. ✓
$(v - u) \times t = \text{gradient}$ ✗

(ii) Area under graph is the displacement ✓

$$x = \frac{1}{2}(u + v)t ✓$$

(iii) $v = u + at$ $x = \frac{1}{2}(u + v)t$ ✓

$$x = \frac{1}{2}ut + vt + u + at ✗ \text{ Incorrect working}$$

$$x = ut + \frac{1}{2}at^2$$

(b) (i) $s = ut + \frac{1}{2}at^2$ ✓

$$s = 12 + \frac{1}{2} \times 0.5 \times 12^2 ✗$$

$$s = 48\,\text{m}$$

(ii) $v^2 = u^2 + 2as$ ✓
$$v^2 = 0^2 + 2 \times 0.5 \times 48$$
$$v^2 = 48 \qquad v = \sqrt{48} = 6.93\,\text{m s}^{-1} ✓ \text{ e.c.f.}$$

(c) (i) $v^2 = u^2 + 2as$
$$6.39^2 = 0^2 + 2 \times ? \times 120$$
$$48 = 2 \times ? \times 120$$
$$\frac{48}{2 \times 120} = 0.1\,\text{m s}^{-2} ✗$$

(ii) $0.1 \times 9.81 = 1.59\,\text{N}$ ✗

(d) acceleration (m s^{-2})

Examiner commentary

(a) (i) Tom successfully identified the meaning of the gradient but in his attempt at using the symbols he multiplied by t rather than divided.

(ii) Tom's answer was totally correct.

(iii) The two equations Tom has written will, if correctly combined and v eliminated, lead to the equation $\boldsymbol{x} = ut + \frac{1}{2}at^2$. Hence he gains the first mark. His algebra lets him down, however.

(b) (i) The correct equation is selected – the use of s rather than x is accepted. Tom makes the common mistake of writing $0 \times 12 = 12$ and hence finds the displacement to be 48 m rather than 36 m.

(ii) Tom's working here is correct. It is not the easiest method of calculating v [$v = u + at$ is more straightforward], but the equation he uses is correct. He has used his [incorrect] value of $\boldsymbol{s}$ but is credited with full marks on the e.c.f. principle.

(c) Tom appears to be calculating the acceleration in part (i). If he had gone on to use this to calculate $\boldsymbol{t}$ he could have received credit for both parts. However, he doesn't and in part 2 goes on to calculate a force instead of the acceleration and unfortunately receives no credit at all.

(d) Tom receives marks for the two horizontal portions of the graph. He receives no credit for the scales because the scale on the time axis is not valid – and the graph doesn't encompass the whole journey.

(e) (i) Tom correctly calculates the value of air resistance at the maximum velocity.

(ii) Tom has just divided the maximum air resistance by 2. The air resistance should have been divided by 4 and the 8 N frictional force added to it.

Tom gains 10 out of 21 marks.

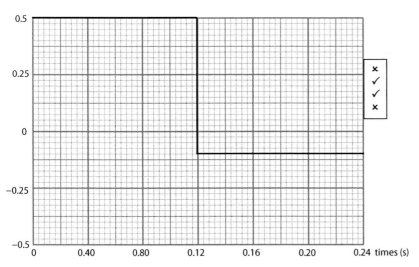

(e) (i) $165 - 8.0 = 157\,\text{N P}$ ✓

(ii) $6.9 = 165\,\text{N}$
$3.45 = 82.5\,\text{N O}$

Q&A 3

A heavy sledge is pulled across a level snowfield by a force F as shown. To keep the sledge moving at a constant velocity a **horizontal** force component of 200 N is required.

(a) Calculate the force needed to produce a horizontal component of 200 N on the sledge. *[2]*

(b) (i) Define work done and use this definition to explain why no work is done in the vertical direction. *[3]*

    (ii) It takes 30 minutes to pull the sledge a distance of 2.0 km across level ground. Calculate:

        (I) the work done;

        (II) the mean power needed. *[4]*

(c) Assume the force F calculated in (a) is now applied horizontally as shown. Calculate the initial acceleration of the sledge, given that its mass is 40.0 kg and assuming that the frictional force stays the same. *[3]*

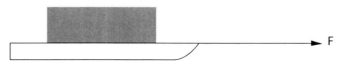

Seren's answer

(a) $\cos 40 = \dfrac{200}{F}$ ✓

    $F = 261$ N ✓

(b) (i) Work done = $Fx \cos\theta$ ✓✓

    Force applied in the desired direction. As no vertical motion is desired ✗ it is not work done.

  (ii) (I) Work done = $Fx \cos\theta$

                = 200 N × 2000 m = 400 000 J ✓✓

    (II) 30 minutes = 1800 s ✓

        $P = \dfrac{E}{t} = \dfrac{400000}{1800} = 222$ W ✓

(c) $a = \dfrac{\Sigma F}{m}$. $\Sigma F = 261$ N $- 200$ N ✓ $= 61$ N

    $a = \dfrac{61}{40}$ ✓ $= 1.5$ m s⁻¹. ✗ (unit penalty)

Examiner commentary

(a) Clearly set out – both marks

(b) (i) Seren's statement, $Fx \cos\theta$, is accepted for 2 marks – the 1st mark is for force × distance and the 2nd for '... moved in the direction of the force' – the cos θ is treated as equivalent to the 2nd statement.

    Strange expression: 'desired' is unclear and not accepted.

  (ii) (I) The 1st mark is a conversion mark [2.0 km → 2000 m] and the second for the correct multiplication.

    (II) Again, Seren has correctly converted 30 minutes to seconds and followed this by a correct application of the power equation.

(c) Seren has calculated the resultant force [1st mark] and correctly applied $a = \dfrac{\Sigma F}{m}$ [2nd mark]. She has given an incorrect unit for acceleration and has missed the 3rd mark.

Seren gains 10 out of 12 marks.

Tom's answer

(a) $\cos 40 = \dfrac{200}{F}$ ✓

$F = 200\cos 40 = 153\,\text{N}$ ✗

(b) (i) Work done = Force × distance moved ✓ ✗

There is no work done vertically because the sledge doesn't move vertically, only horizontally. ✓

(ii) (I) $2000\,\text{m}$ ✓ $\times 200\,\text{N} = 40{,}000\,\text{J}$ ✗

(II) $60 \times 60 = 3600$ (1 minute)

$3600 \times 30 = 108{,}000$ (30 minutes) ✗

$P = \dfrac{W}{t} = \dfrac{40{,}000}{108{,}000}$ ✓ e.c.f. $= 0.37\,\text{W}$

(c) $F = ma$

$153 = 40 \times a$ ✗

$\dfrac{153}{40} = a = 3.8\,\text{m s}^{-2}$ ✗ no e.c.f.

Examiner commentary

(a) Tom has correctly substituted into the equation, gaining the 1st mark, but has re-arranged incorrectly and so loses the 2nd mark.

(b) (i) The definition of work done is incomplete because there is no statement about direction of motion. The subsequent statement is insufficient to overcome this deficit.

Tom gains the 3rd mark, however, because he correctly identifies that there is no vertical motion.

(ii) (I) Tom correctly converts 2.0 km to m but makes a slip in multiplying.

(II) Tom loses the 1st mark for the minute → second conversion but is allowed e.c.f. on both this and the incorrect work in the calculation of power.

(c) In this last part of the question, the examiners only gave any credit if candidates attempted to calculate the resultant force. As Tom didn't do this he received 0 for part (c).

Tom gains 5 out of 12 marks.

(a) Derive, giving a labelled diagram, the relationship between the current I through a metal wire of cross-sectional area A, the drift velocity, v, of the free electrons, each of charge e, and the number, n, of free electrons per unit volume of the metal. *[4]*

$(I = nAve)$

(b) Calculate the drift velocity of free electrons in a copper wire of cross-sectional area $1.7 \times 10^{-6}\,\text{m}^2$ when a current of 2.0 A flows. [$n_{copper} = 1.0 \times 10^{29}\,\text{m}^{-3}$]. *[2]*

(c) A potential is required across the copper in order for the current to flow. The size of the current depends upon the wire's *resistance*. Explain in terms of free electrons, how this resistance arises. *[2]*

(d) The copper wire in (b) is of length 2.5 m. When it carries a current of 2.0 A it dissipates energy at the rate of 0.1 W. Calculate its resistivity. *[4]*

(e) A second copper wire has the same volume as the wire in (d) but is longer. Complete the table below indicating whether the quantity given is **bigger**, **smaller** or **the same** for this longer wire. *[3]*

Quantity	For the longer wire this quantity is:
Cross-sectional area	
n, the number of free electrons / unit volume	
Resistivity	

Seren's answer

(a)

✓

Q = number of electrons × charge on each electron

$Q = V \times n \times e$ ✓

since $V = Al$ $Q = Alne$ ✓

$I = \dfrac{Q}{t}$ $\therefore I = \dfrac{Alne}{t}$

since $v = \dfrac{l}{t}$ $I = nAve$ ✓

(b) $v = \dfrac{I}{nAe}$ $v = \dfrac{2.0}{1.0 \times 10^{29} \times 1.7 \times 10^{-6} \times 1.6 \times 10^{-19}}$ ✓

$v = 7.4 \times 10^{-5} \text{ m s}^{-1}$ ✓

(c) The free electrons that travel in the wire collide ✓ with ions ✓, which give its resistance. If, for example, the copper is heated, it means the ions vibrate more in a sphere of influence, and more electrons collide with them, giving higher resistance.

(d) $\rho = \dfrac{RA}{l}$ $P = I^2R$ ✓ $\therefore R = \dfrac{P}{I^2} = \dfrac{0.1}{2.0^2} = 0.025\ \Omega.$ ✓

$\rho = \dfrac{0.025 \times 1.7 \times 10^{-6}}{2.5}$ ✓ $= 1.7 \times 10^{-8}\ \Omega\,\text{m}^{-1}$ ✓ [note incorrect unit]

(e) same   ✗

same   ✓

smaller   ✗

Examiner commentary

(a) Not a perfect derivation; for example, *l* is not defined, and there is no commentary, but the answer hits all the marking points.

(b) First mark for substitution into the equation – Seren has manipulated the equation too, which was not necessary for this mark – and the second for the correct answer.

(c) Seren has answered the question in the first sentence. The second sentence answers a different question.

(d) Seren identifies the resistivity equation, realises she needs first to find the resistance, which she correctly does using $P = I^2R$, and then goes on to calculate the resistivity. She uses the wrong unit for resistivity but is lucky that, on this occasion, there was no unit penalty!

(e) Seren has not realised that, if the volume of the longer wire is the same as that of the shorter wire, its cross sectional area must be less! The resistivity is a characteristic of the <u>material</u> and does not depend upon the shape of the specimen.

Seren gains 13 out of 15 marks.

Tom's answer

(a)

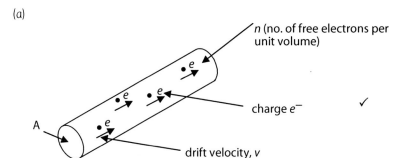

n (no. of free electrons per unit volume)

charge e^- ✓

A

drift velocity, v

$I = nAve$ for current   velocity $= \dfrac{I}{nAe}$ $n = \dfrac{I}{Ave}$

$A = \dfrac{I}{nev}$ $e = \dfrac{I}{Ane}$

(b) $v = \dfrac{I}{nAe}$

$= \dfrac{2.0}{1.7 \times 10^{-6} \times 1.0 \times 10^{-16} \times 1.0 \times 10^{29}}$ ✗ – incorrect substitution

$= 1.176 \times 10^{-7}$ m s^{-1} ✗ – no e.c.f.

(c) Free electrons in the wire knock into ✓ ions in the metal lattice ✓ they block the way and slow electrons down giving resistance.

(d) $R = \dfrac{V}{I}$. $P = VI$ so $R = \dfrac{I^2}{P} = \dfrac{4}{0.1} = 40\,\Omega$

$\rho = \dfrac{RA}{I} = \dfrac{40 \times 1.7 \times 10^{-6}}{2.5}$ ✓ (e.c.f.) $= 2.72 \times 10^{-5}\,\Omega$ m ✓

(e) smaller   ✓
same   ✓
smaller   ✗

Examiner commentary

(a) Good diagram – excessive labelling as the quantities are defined in the question stem. Tom clearly has not learnt the derivation. He has just played with the equation.

(b) Tom has made a mistake with his substitution – the value for e is wrong. He has not helped himself by not keeping the quantities on the bottom line of the fraction in the same order as that in the algebraic equation. The second mark cannot be given following an incorrect substitution.

(c) Tom has given a satisfactory answer here.

(d) Tom has made a mistake in finding R. His use of this incorrect value was credited on the e.c.f. principle and therefore so was his incorrect final answer.

(e) The resistivity of a metal does not depend upon its shape – only the composition.

Tom gains 7 out of 15 marks.

(a) What is a superconductor? [1]

(b) With the aid of a sketch graph, explain the term superconducting transition temperature. [3]

(c) Explain why superconductors are useful for applications which require large electric currents and name **one** such application. [2]

5

Seren's answer

(a) A material that, beyond a certain temperature, its resistance falls effectively to 0. ✓bod

(b)

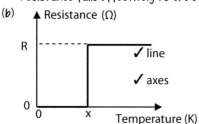

x is the temperature beyond which the resistance effectively becomes 0. A transition between resistance R and 0 occurs at this temperature. ✓

(c) A large amount of current can pass through them easily (i.e. they will feel no resistance). They are used in particle accelerators. ✓

Examiner commentary

(a) On this occasion the examiner was only looking for the 0 resistance – the idea of transition temperature is covered in (b).

(b) Seren has correctly identified the axes and given a correct graph. 'Beyond' is not a good word to use, but it is clear from the graph that she means 'below'.

(c) The missing mark is because no link was made to 0 energy loss with a superconductor. Particle accelerators was accepted for the mark but ideally Seren would have identified the magnets as requiring the superconductors.

Seren gains 5 out of 6 marks.

Tom's answer

(a) A conductor with zero resistance. ✓

(b)

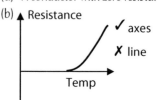

This is the temperature at which all resistance disappears. ✗

(c) Power cables – less energy is wasted through friction/heat ✓ ∴ they are more efficient.

Examiner commentary

(a) Tom hits the marking point.

(b) Tom has correctly identified that the significant graph is one of resistance against temperature but has drawn an inadequate line and his description does not make it clear that the 0 resistance covers a range of temperatures from 0 to the transition temperature.

(c) Tom identifies the advantage as involving energy loss ['friction' is ignored here] but it was not accepted that power cables use superconductors.

Tom gains 3 out of 6 marks.

A student directs a narrow beam of light on to one end of a glass block, as shown:

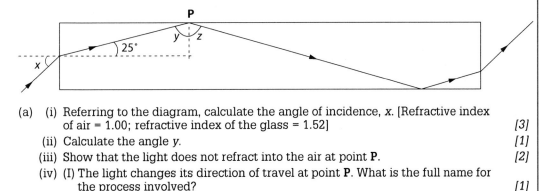

(a) (i) Referring to the diagram, calculate the angle of incidence, x. [Refractive index of air = 1.00; refractive index of the glass = 1.52] [3]

    (ii) Calculate the angle y. [1]

    (iii) Show that the light does not refract into the air at point **P**. [2]

    (iv) (I) The light changes its direction of travel at point **P**. What is the full name for the process involved? [1]

        (II) How does the size of the angle z compare with the size of angle y? [1]

(b) (i) A glass fibre used for the transmission of data consists of a central glass core with a *cladding* of glass of lower refractive index. Suggest one advantage of having glass cladding rather than simply an air surround. [1]

    (ii) What can be said about the diameter of a monomode fibre? [2]

    (iii) Why is such a fibre called monomode? [1]

Seren's answer

(a) (i) $n_1 \sin\theta_1 = n_2 \sin\theta_2$

$\therefore 1 \sin x = 1.52 \sin 25$ ✓; $\therefore \sin x = 0.6423...$

$\therefore x = \sin^{-1} 0.642$ ✓ $= 40.0°$ (to 3.s.f.) ✓

(ii) $180 - (25 + 90) = 65°$ ✓

(iii) $n_1 \sin\theta_1 = n_2 \sin 90$

$\therefore 1.52 \sin\theta_1 = n_2$ ✓ $\therefore$ critical angle $= \sin\left(\dfrac{1}{1.52}\right) = 41.1°$

$\therefore 65° >$ critical angle (41.1°) ✓

$\therefore$ light does not refract

(iv) (I) Total internal reflection. ✓

    (II) $z = y$ ✓

(b) (i) It reduces the critical angle, thereby reducing the amount of paths .✗ not b.o.d.

(ii) It is very small ✓

(iii) It only allows one path for transmission. ✓

Examiner commentary

(a) (i) The first mark is for putting correct data into the equation; the second for the answer.

    (iii) Seren has applied the correct principle: 1st mark – correct insertion into the equation; 2nd mark for the correct discussion.

(b) (i) This is a statement in the right area [effect on critical angle] but it is the wrong way round (cladding will <u>increase</u> the critical angle) and there is no link to the linked advantage, i.e. reduction of multimode dispersion.

    (ii) This is the first marking point. The second required an approximate size [less than ~ 1 µm was accepted] or a comment about the size in relation to the wavelength of the radiation used.

    (iii) A rare correct statement!

Seren gains 10 out of 12 marks.

Tom's answer

(a) (i) $n = \dfrac{sin i}{sin r} = \dfrac{sin 1}{sin 1.52}$ ✗ $= 0.647$ $sin^{-1} = 41°$

(ii) $130 \div 2 = 65°$ ✓

(iii) Because for the light to refract out into the air, angle x must be smaller for the light to not refract inwards but go outwards instead. ✗

(iv) (I) Total internal refraction ✗

(II) They are the same size. ✓

(b) (i) It means that only beams with small angles of incidence stay inside the fibre, so all the beams inside arrive at their destination at similar times. ✓

(ii) Very small ✓

(iii) Only one bit of information can be passed down it. ✗

Examiner commentary

(a) (i) Tom has selected a version of the correct formula but has missed the first mark because he has inserted incorrect data. No mark can be given for the answer resulting from this.

(ii) The answer is correct: the method is slightly obscure but not demonstrably incorrect.

(iii) Tom fails to realise that a calculation is needed here. The comment about x is irrelevant as it is the angle y which is significant.

(iv) (I) Tom has used the word 'refraction' instead of 'reflection' – this confusion also occurs in the answer to (a) (iii) – no e.c.f. is allowed for this mistake of principle.

(b) (i) A good answer from a weak student.

(ii) As Seren's answer.

(iii) A common misunderstanding.

Tom gains 4 out of 12 marks.

(a) (i) What is the *photoelectric effect*? [2]

(ii) Give an account of the photoelectric effect in terms of photons, electrons and energy, explaining how it leads to *Einstein's photoelectric equation*. [4]

(b) (i) A zinc surface of work function 4.97×10^{-19} J is irradiated with two frequencies of electromagnetic radiation in turn. For each frequency, show whether or not electrons are emitted from the surface and, if they are emitted, calculate their maximum kinetic energy.

(I) 7.99×10^{14} Hz. [2]

(II) 6.74×10^{14} Hz [1]

(ii) What would be the maximum kinetic energy of the electrons emitted if the surface were irradiated with both frequencies at once? Explain your reasoning. [2]

Seren's answer

(a) (i) The emission of an electron from the metal surface ✓ with the energy provided by photon energy of light source. ✓

(ii) The energy of a photon required to liberate ✓ an electron should be equal to either the work function (minimum) ✓ or more (work function = minimum energy to liberate an electron). For photons with greater energy than the work function, the kinetic energy of the liberated electron is equal to the difference between E_{photon} and ϕ, ✓ i.e. $KE_{max} = hf - \phi$, where hf = photon energy ✓ and ϕ = work function.

(b) (i) (I) Photon energy = $6.63 \times 10^{-34} \times 7.99 \times 10^{14} = 5.297 \times 10^{-19}$

It is bigger than ϕ and so electrons are emitted. ✓

Max KE = $5.297 \times 10^{-19} - 4.97 \times 10^{-14} = 3.27 \times 10^{-20}$ J ✓

(II) Photon energy = $6.63 \times 10^{-34} \times 6.74 \times 10^{14}$

= $4.47 \times 10^{-19} < \phi$

So no electron is emitted. ✓

(ii) 3.27×10^{-20} J, because the metal will absorb the light with the higher frequency for emitting electrons. ✓✓

Examiner commentary

(a) (i) Electrons from metal surface; energy provided by photons – 2 clear marks

(ii) The account is rambling, but all the marking points are covered: photon energy; work function; indication that a single photon liberates a single electron; clear statement of energy housekeeping.

(b) (i) (I) Seren's statement is different from Tom's and equally valid.

(II) Seren has shown clearly that the photon has insufficient energy and drawn the correct conclusion.

(ii) Seren's answer is not perfect, but enough for the mark: she has correctly given the energy; a statement that the photon energies cannot combine, or similar, would have been better.

Seren gains 11 out of 11 marks.

Tom's answer

(a) (i) When photons of the correct energy are absorbed and electrons are emitted. ✗✓

(ii) Einstein's photo-electric equation: $\frac{1}{2}mv^2 = hf - \phi$

$\frac{1}{2}mv^2$ is the maximum kinetic energy of electron

hf is the frequency of photon. ✗

ϕ is the minimum energy needed to remove the electron from the surface ✓

– sign is the energy escape left.

(b) (i) (I) $E = hf - \phi = 6.63 \times 10^{-34} \times 7.99 \times 10^{14} - 4.97 \times 10^{-14}$ ✓

= 3.27×10^{-20} J ∴ Electrons are emitted. ✓

(II) $E = hf - \phi = 6.63 \times 10^{-34} \times 6.74 \times 10^{14} - 4.97 \times 10^{-14}$

= -5.01×10^{-20} J ✗

(ii) It will be equal to zero as the frequency is minimum. ✗

Examiner commentary

(a) (i) The absorption/emission mark is awarded, but not the context.

(ii) It's a good idea to state the equation but the derivation should be clear. The identification of ϕ is clear and gains a mark. Tom calls hf the 'frequency' of the photon – 'energy' would have gained the extra mark.

Unfortunately the mark scheme awarded no mark for $\frac{1}{2}mv^2$ and the last statement needs too much interpretation to credit.

(b) (i) (I) Good – clear and concise. Tom derives the maximum energy of the emitted electrons and states that they are emitted.

(II) There is no mark just for repeating a calculation. Tom should have drawn attention to the – sign and indicated that no electrons would be emitted.

(ii) This statement has no worth.

Tom gains 4 out of 11 marks.

In the helium-neon laser, excited helium atoms collide with neon atoms and transfer energy to them. This raises neon atoms from the ground state to the excited *metastable* state, **U** (see diagram).

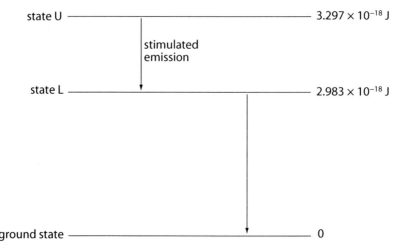

Photons are emitted by stimulated emission involving an electron transition between state **U** and state **L**.

(a) (i) Calculate the fraction

$$\frac{\text{photon energy}}{\text{energy used to excite atom to level } \textbf{U}}$$

[2]

   (ii) Calculate the wavelength of the light emitted. [2]

(b) (i) What causes a stimulated emission even to occur? [2]

   (ii) Describe carefully, in terms of photons, the outcome of such an event. [2]

   (iii) The electron stays in level **L** for only a very short time, spontaneously dropping to the ground state. Explain why this feature is important to the operation of a laser. [2]

   (iv) The mixture of helium and neon is contained in a long cavity with mirrors, as shown in the simplified diagram.

mirror reflecting almost 100% of light   *amplifying medium* of helium and neon   mirror reflecting almost 99% of light

How does this cavity design promote laser operation? [2]

Seren's answer

(a) (i) photon energy = $3.297 \times 10^{-18} - 2.983 \times 10^{-18}$ ✓ = 3.14×10^{-19} J

$\therefore$ Fraction = $\dfrac{3.14 \times 10^{-19}}{3.297 \times 10^{-18}} = \dfrac{2}{21}$ ✓

(ii) $E_{photon} = \dfrac{hc}{\lambda} \therefore \lambda = \dfrac{hc}{E_{photon}}$ ✓ $= \dfrac{6.6 \times 10^{-34} \times 3 \times 10^{8}}{3.14 \times 10^{-19}}$

$= 6.31 \times 10^{-7}$ m ✓

(b) (i) An incident photon on an atom ✓ causes it to rise to an excited state then quickly drop down, releasing a photon, which causes a knock-on effect on other excited states ✗

(ii) The knock on effect of photons being released at practically the same time causes all photons to be coherent ✓ with each other causing light amplification (which is monochromatic).

(iii) It makes a population inversion easier to achieve. ✓ If there was no population inversion, then there will be more absorbtion than emission ✓ and the amplifying medium will not function.

(iv) It allows photons to move back and forth within the amplifying medium ✓ and $\therefore$ increase in intensity ✓ while allowing 1% of light out, to carry out the function of the particular laser.

Examiner commentary

(a) (i) Clearly laid out: the desired answer was 0.095 but most candidates gave $\dfrac{2}{21}$ and this was accepted.

(ii) Correct equation produced for λ (1st mark); correct answer (2nd mark).

(b) (i) Seren has identified the event as being caused by an incident photon but has mistakenly stated that this causes excitation.

(ii) Seren's answer is not worth two marks because it fails to deal with a single event, i.e. a single photon incident leading to 2 photons emerging.

(iii) Seren's is an excellent response. The spelling mistake, even in a significant word, is ignored.

(iv) Seren's answer picks out both marking points clearly – see Tom's answer and Examiner commentary.

Seren gains 10 out of 12 marks.

Tom's answer

(a) (i) $\dfrac{3.297}{(3.297 - 2.983)} = \dfrac{21}{2}$ ✗

(ii) $E = hf, E = h\left(\dfrac{c}{\lambda}\right)$ $\therefore 3.14 \times 10^{-19} = 6.63 \times 10^{-34} \times \left(\dfrac{3 \times 10^{8}}{\lambda}\right)$

$\lambda = 6.33 \times 10^{-7}$ m ✓✓

(b) (i) A photon hitting the electron encouraging it to drop to a lower energy. ✓

(ii) The photon will be of the same frequency ✓ as the one that hit it and they ✓ will be in phase.

(iii) The photon emitted does not cause stimulated emission but spontaneous emission, which will <u>not</u> cause coherent photons to be emitted. ✗

(iv) Most photons produced will reflect back and stimulate more with the same frequency. ✓

Examiner commentary

(a) (i) How unfortunate! Tom has noticed that the factor of 10^{-18} is common, so can be omitted, but has inverted the fraction. No credit gained.

(ii) The first mark is for combining the equations $E = hf$ and $c = f\lambda$ and manipulating to produce an equation with λ as the subject; the second mark for the answer.

(b) (i) Tom has, somewhat clumsily, identified an event as being caused by an incident photon. He has missed the point that the photon's energy must equal the energy gap U–L.

(ii) Tom has identified that the stimulated photon will have the same frequency as the incoming one [better would have been or 'coherent']. His comment that 'they will be in phase' implies that there are two photons where previously there was one.

(iii) Tom does not address the importance of population inversion.

(iv) Tom has partly addressed two marking points (multiple traverses of the cavity; increasing the chances of stimulated emission) and is credited with one mark.

Tom gains 6 out of 12 marks.

Q&A 9

When 2 protons are accelerated to high kinetic energies and collide with each other, the following reaction may occur. [**x** is an 'unknown' particle.]

$$p + p \rightarrow p + x + \pi^+$$

(a) The charge on a proton (p) is $+e$.
   (i) What is the magnitude of the charge on the π^+ (a pion or π meson)? [1]
   (ii) Determine the charge of particle **x**. [1]
(b) The π^+ is classed as a *meson*. How is p classed? [1]
(c) In the reaction, u quark number and d quark number are each conserved.
[$\bar{u}$ is assigned a u quark number of −1, and $\bar{d}$ a d quark number of −1.]
Giving your reasoning, determine the quark make-up of particle **x** and hence identify this particle. [4]
(d) Explain how *lepton* conservation applies in this reaction. [1]
(e) Discuss which of the forces, *weak*, *strong* or *electromagnetic*, is likely to be responsible for the reaction. [2]

Seren's answer

(a) (i) +1, +e ✓
   (ii) 0e, neutral ✓
(b) baryon ✓
(c) quark formula: uud + uud → uud + x + u$\bar{d}$
   ✓ for the protons, ✓ for the pion
   so quark make up of x is udd. ✓ The particle is a neutron. ✓
(d) The overall lepton number of each side is 0 as no leptons are present. ✓
(e) The strong force ✓ is likely to be responsible because quarks are the only particles present in the reaction – there are no leptons. ✓

Examiner commentary

(c) Reasonably full working – Seren has clearly given the quark make-up of the protons and pion and identified the resulting particle and its composition.
(d) This is a much clearer statement than Tom's.
(e) The second sentence doesn't quite pin it down but weak interactions involving only quarks are possible – but only when individual quark flavours are not conserved, this is not on the specification but Seren's answer receives full credit.

Seren gains 10 out of 10 marks.

Tom's answer

(a) (i) +1 ✓
   (ii) 0 ✓
(b) quarks ✗
(c) ↑↑↓ + ↑↑↓ → ↑↑↓ + ↑↓↓
   up, down, down ✓ with a charge of 0 is a neutron ✓
(d) There is always 0 ✗
(e) Strong force ✓
   Because protons and neutrons are present in the product formula which can form an attractive or repulsive force between them. ✗?

Examiner commentary

(a) (i) Either +1 or +e was accepted.
   (ii) No explanation is required on this occasion. 0, 0e or neutral were accepted.
(b) The particle contains quarks – it is classed as a baryon.
(c) The first line was not credited – the notation clearly represents up and down quarks but the meson is missing and it is not clear how it relates to the answers, which are correct. 'Giving your reasoning' means that the examiner needs to be convinced.
(d) It is not clear what this means.
(e) The second sentence may mean something, but again it is not clear.

Tom gains 5 out of 10 marks.

Q&A 10

(a) (i) The spectrum of the star Rigel in the constellation of Orion peaks at a wavelength of 260 nm. Calculate the temperature of the surface of Rigel. *[2]*

    (ii) What assumptions were you making about the way the star's surface radiates? *[1]*

(b) To a good approximation, the kelvin temperature of Rigel's surface is twice that of the Sun, and the radius of Rigel is 70 times the radius of the Sun. Use Stefan's Law to estimate the ratio:

$$\frac{\text{total power of electromagnetic radiation emitted by Rigel}}{\text{total power of electromagnetic radiation emitted by the Sun}}$$ *[3]*

(c) We can discover the presence of particular atoms in the atmosphere of a star by measuring the wavelengths of dark lines in the star's spectrum.
Explain how the lines arise, and why they occur at specific wavelengths. *[3]*

Seren's answer

(a) (i) $\lambda_{max}T = W$

    $250 \times 10^{-9} \times T = 2.90 \times 10^{-3}$ ✓

    $T = 11154°$ ✗ (unit)

    (ii) It radiates as a black body. ✓

(b) Rigel $r = 70$ Sun $= 1$

$P_R = 4\pi \times 70^2 \times 5.67 \times 10^{-8} \times 11154^4 = 5.402 \times 10^{13}$

$P_S = 4\pi \times 1^2 \times 5.67 \times 10^{-8} \times (\frac{1}{2} \times 11154)^4 = 6.89 \times 10^8$ ✓✓

Ratio $= \dfrac{5.40 \times 10^{13}}{6.89 \times 10^8}$, so Rigel $= 78374$ times more power

than the Sun ✓

(c) Radiation of all wavelengths is emitted from the star. The photons emitted pass through the atmosphere of the star. ✓ If a photon collides with an electron and the photon's energy coincides with an energy gap jump for the electron, the photon is absorbed ✓ by the electron jumping to a higher energy level. This shows up as a dark vertical line on the coloured spectrum at the wavelength absorbed. ✓

Examiner commentary

(a) (i) Seren correctly calculates the kelvin value of the temperature. Unfortunately she omits the unit - ° is not a unit.

(b) Seren uses the relative values of radius, and correctly squares this ratio. She raises the temperatures to the 4th power. She calculates the two powers – the fact that she does not use actual radii and hence does not express the powers in SI units does not matter: she correctly finds the ratio.

(c) Seren correctly identifies:
- that the radiation with a continuous spectrum passes through the atmosphere of a star;
- absorption happens by interaction with atoms with a specific energy gap
- the dark line corresponds to the energy of the absorbed photons.

Seren scores 8 out of 9 marks

Tom's answer

(a) (i) $\lambda_{max} = WT^{-1}$

    $250 \times 10^{-9} = 2.90 \times 10^{-3}\, T^{-1}$ ✓

    $T^{-1} = 8.97 \times 10^{-5}.$ $T = 1.13 \times 10^4$ K ✓

    (ii) Temperature is the same over the surface ✗

(b) $T_R = 2T_S;\ R_R = 70R_S$

$P = A\sigma T^4.$ $\dfrac{P_R}{P_S} = \dfrac{4\pi r^2 \times \sigma \times T^4}{4\pi r^2 \times \sigma \times T^4} = \dfrac{r^2 \times T^4}{r^2 \times T^4}$ [π and σ are the same]

$= \dfrac{1^2 \times 11200^4}{70^2 \times \left(\dfrac{11200}{2}\right)^4}$ ✓ ✗

$= \dfrac{4}{1125} = 3.27 \times 10^{-3}$

(c) A continuous spectrum is given off from a star but an absorption spectrum is seen when looking at the star. This is because gases absorb certain wavelengths of light. ✓
∴ we can discover what gas a star is made up from.

Examiner commentary

(a) (i) Tom selects the correct equation and substitutes data correctly, earning the first mark. He correctly calculates the temperature and gives the unit, earning the second mark.

    (ii) Tom misses the point that Wien's Law is only true for black bodies.

(b) Tom correctly expresses Stefan's Law to obtain the ratio. He correctly handles the 4th power of the temperatures and gains a mark but unfortunately inverts the ratio of the square of the radii. Thus his final answer is incorrect. Tom's initial statement, $T_R = 2T_S$, is correct but he does not use it.

(c) To obtain more than one mark, Tom needs to discuss the absorption of photons / atomic energy levels and also to indicate where the absorption occurs.

Tom scores 4 out of 9 marks

Quickfire answers

PH1

① $[s] = $ m; $[ut] = $ m s^{-1}s = m; $[\frac{1}{2}at^2]$
    = m s^{-2} s^2 = m

② kg m^{-1} s^{-2}

③ kg m^{-1} (or N m^{-2} s^2)

④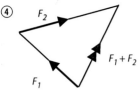

⑤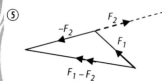

⑥ Any 2 from the list of scalars (e.g. density and mass) and vectors (e.g. displacement and velocity). A vector has magnitude [size] and direction; a scalar has magnitude only.

⑦ 1.6 m s^{-2} to the left. [Note: direction!]

⑧ 2960 N
Note that the size of the velocity is irrelevant – if the velocity is constant, the resultant force is zero.

⑨ 53.0 m s^{-2}, in a direction 23.5° upwards to the left.

⑩ H – 1.8 m s^{-2}, V – 2.9 m s^{-2}; H – 98 m; V – 85 m

⑪ $E = 5.95$ N C^{-1}; $E_v = 2.7$ N C^{-1}

⑫ 19 300 N

⑬ 1.7 m s^{-2}

⑭ Air resistance: Forward resistive force of the aeroplane on the surrounding air.
Weight: Upward gravitational force of the plane on the Earth.
Note – always mention the body upon which the force acts.

⑮ Notes: The shape of the 'car' doesn't matter. For these questions, the exact positions of the force arrows don't matter, but their tails should all touch the body.

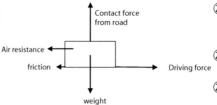

⑯ 56 m^3

⑰ Zero resultant force; zero resultant moment about any point.
Note remember 'about any point'.

⑱ The friction between the tyres and the ground.

⑲ (i) Stationary
    (ii) 92 m s^{-1}
    (iii) 1100 m s^{-2}
    (iv) 1000 m s^{-2}

⑳ (i) See graph – note that the vertical lines are optional.
    (ii) Distance = 0.71 m.

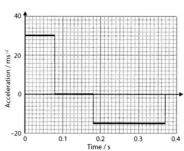

㉑ $v^2 = u^2 + ax \rightarrow (u + at)^2$
    $= u^2 + 2ax \rightarrow u^2 + 2uat + a^2t^2$
    $= u^2 + 2ax$
    $2uat + a^2t^2 = 2ax \rightarrow 2ut + at^2$
    $= 2x \rightarrow x$
    $= ut + \frac{1}{2}at^2$ QED

㉒ $x = vt - \frac{1}{2}at^2$

㉓ Initially there is no air resistance, so the resultant force = mg. So the acceleration is g, i.e. 9.81 m s^{-2}.

㉔ Air resistance increases with speed. When the total of the air resistance and friction is 10 000 N, the resultant force is zero, so there is no acceleration.

㉕ 16

㉖ (i) 0, –6.7 m s^{-1}
    (ii) –6.7 m s^{-1}, –9.2 m s^{-1}
    (iii) 0, –9.2 m s^{-1}

㉗ 14.1 m s^{-1} at an angle of 40.1° below the horizontal

㉘ (i) 17.5 m s^{-1} [both!]
    (ii) 1.78 s
    (iii) 15.6 m
    (iv) 62.3 m

㉙ 126 m

㉚ Venus always moves at right angles to the force so cos $\theta = 0$

㉛ 700 kW

㉜ 49 N m^{-1}

㉝ 0.036 m; 0.055 J

㉞ 9 MJ

㉟ 4.7×10^{-26} kg

㊱ 92 m s^{-1} [impressive]

㊲ 500 m s^{-1}

㊳ 7.8 g

㊴ (i) 14.3 MJ
    (ii) 14.3 MJ
    (iii) 243 kN
    (iv) Initial KE = final thermal energy of brakes (excluding other losses).
    (v) The final useful energy is 0 (thermal energy of brakes is useless) so efficiency is 0.

㊵ (i) 18.2 kJ
    (ii) 332 N
    (iii) 79 N

㊶ The water resistance increases with speed. When it is equal to the thrust, the work needed to overcome the water resistance each second is equal to the work done by the thrust, so no increase in kinetic energy occurs.

㊷ It is transferred to air molecules, initially as kinetic energy in air turbulence and finally to random thermal motion of the air molecules.

㊸ The molecules in the duster attract electrons more strongly than those in the cellulose acetate. When the two are rubbed, some electrons, which are negatively charged, are transferred from the acetate to the duster. This leaves the acetate with fewer electrons than protons and so is positively charged. The duster initially has an equal and opposite negative charge, but this quickly leaks away.

㊹ Electrons in the paper feel an attractive force and move towards the positively charge rod. This gives a negative charge on the parts of paper nearest the rod and a positive charge on the parts further away. The attraction between the positive rod and the negative parts of the paper will be greater than the repulsion due to the positive rod and the positive parts of the paper (because of the different distances). Hence there will be an overall attractive force.

㊺ The negative charges repel one another. Because these charges can move through the metal conductor, they push each other to the outside of the metal.

㊻ 6.25×10^{18}

㊼ 41 s

㊽ 35 A

㊾ Hint: calculate the cross-sectional area and hence the diameter. 33 s.w.g.

㊿ 336 J

(51) (i) 5.9 V
(ii) 5.76 C
(iii) 34 J

(52) 7.3 W

(53) 13.0 A

(54) 960 W

(55) As the temperature increases, electrons travel faster (in between collisions) and the metal ions vibrate more. This decreases the time in between collisions and hence, the drift velocity. The current decreases and hence the resistance has increased.

(56) (Answer in question) – remember that you have the wire diameter and that the mm should be converted to metres (2.55×10^{-4} m)

(57) $490 \times 10^{-9}\ \Omega\,\text{m}$

(58) From the equation $R = \frac{\rho l}{A}$ the gradient of the line will be $\frac{\rho}{A}$.
So you will need to multiply the gradient by A (the cross-sectional area).

(59) 0.5 A

(60) 1.98 V (left resistor) and 0.99 V across the other two.

(61) $29\ \Omega = (18 + 33 \div 3)$

(62) $4.06\ \Omega$

(63) 0.119 V

(64) $R = 105\ \Omega$

(65) E = 1.65 V, gradient = internal resistance = $2.5\ \Omega$, Max current = 0.66 A ($1.65 \div 2.5$)

PH2

① 50 Hz, 0.020 s

② $6.0\ \text{m s}^{-1}$ (because $\lambda = 4.0$ m, $f = 1.5$ Hz)

③ Because door width roughly equal to λ_{sound}, but door width >> λ_{light}.

④ For 100 MHz, $\lambda = 3$ m, so valley 'width' >> λ,
For 1 MHz, $\lambda = 300$ m so more diffraction

⑤ 0.86 m

⑥ $4.0\ \text{m s}^{-1}$

⑦ $2.26 \times 10^{8}\ \text{m s}^{-1}$

⑧ 32° (It is not a coincidence that this is the same as with glass 'in the way'.)

⑨ 24°

⑩ 70°

⑪ 20°

⑫ 13.5 μs (8.3 μs comes from wrongly taking speed in glass as c!)

⑬ 13.7 μs (using AB = AC cos 10°)

⑭ $\frac{3}{2}\lambda$

⑮ The intensity of the fringes follows the diffraction pattern – this is only strong for very small angles

⑯ 630 nm (2 s.f.)

⑰ Yes but bright and dark fringes swap places.

⑱ 2.0×10^{-6} m

⑲ 590 nm (2 s.f.)

⑳ 3

㉑ $384\ \text{m s}^{-1}$

㉒ Second, fourth, sixth … (because each of these would have a node at the middle of the string, but that's where the string is hit!)

㉓ 5×10^{6}

㉔ Microwave oven

㉕ Ionise

㉖ Laser, radio station (though, strictly, both give a narrow band (or bands) of frequencies)

㉗ 1.99×10^{-18} J

㉘ Larger than for red

㉙ 7.7×10^{-20} J

㉚ 5.5×10^{14} Hz

㉛ 6.2×10^{-20} J

㉜ It contains a whole range of frequencies (not even sharply bounded)

㉝ 4.6×10^{14} Hz, 3.1×10^{-19} J,
6.7×10^{-34} Js

㉞ $\frac{\phi}{e}$

㉟ $2.26 \times 10^{16}\ \text{s}^{-1}$, $9.38 \times 10^{12}\ \text{s}^{-1}$,
0.041%

㊱ 663 nm (visible), 121 nm (UV)

㊲ (c) is in the u-v. All other transitions to ground state are of higher energy, so the photons are of shorter wavelength, and in u-v.

㊳ Very high (thousands kelvin!)

㊴ 1.05×10^{-6} m, 2.7×10^{-19} J

㊵ Neutron

㊶ Comparing nucleon numbers, 18/20 = 90%. Relies on mass of neutron being close to that of proton – it is important to state this.

㊷ No – might have one neutron or two neutrons.

㊸ $\bar{\nu}_e$

㊹ e^{+}

㊺ (i) 4, 4 (2 + 2, 2 + 1 + 1)
(ii) 2, 2 (1 + 1, 1 + 2 – 1)

㊻ Not a quark or quark combination (hadron), so can't feel strong force. No charge, so can't feel e-m force.

(47) • e-m (lifetime too long for strong and too short for weak, γ involvement. Also u quark number and/or d-quark number separately conserved and no neutrino involvement so not weak).
• weak ('long' lifetime, neutrino involvement, neither u quark number nor d quark number conserved).
• strong (very short lifetime, no change to u or d quark numbers, no γs).

(48) • visible • borderline visible/infrared • infrared

(49) $3.0[\pm 0.1]\times 10^{-3}$ K m in each case. It confirms Wien's law and the value of the Wien constant, W, since Wien's law may be written $T\lambda_p = W$.

(50) 2.8×10^{10} m

(51) Annihilate with electrons to produce gammas. (This happens deep inside the star and few of these gammas escape from the star.)

PH3 Practical Physics

① 1°

② 17.3 Ω

③ (a) 30.1 cm [measure to resolution of instrument].
(b) 7.5 mA [give the units]
(c) 6.4 W [consistent s.f.]

④ Gradient = 0.028 N mm^{-1}
Intercept = 0.40 N
Some people do not write units for the gradient and intercept. We recommend that you do as it helps you to interpret their significance, e.g. the unit of the gradient of a velocity time graph is m s^{-2}, so it represents an acceleration.

⑤ 1.92 m s^{-2}

⑥ $y_1 \propto \frac{1}{x}$ or $y_1 = \frac{60.0}{x}$;
y_2 is linearly related to x – when x increases by 2.0, y_2 increases by 1.0;
$y_3 \propto x$ or $y = 0.4x$;
$y_4 \propto x^2$ or $y_4 = 0.25x^2$
In each case, both answers are correct but the second gives more information.

⑦ The intercept is 0; the gradient is $\frac{\lambda}{d}$. To find λ, measure the gradient and multiply by d

⑧ (a) $\frac{4\pi^2}{k}$

(b) e.g. T against $\sqrt{m}$ – gradient = $\frac{2\pi}{\sqrt{k}}$, so $k = \frac{4\pi^2}{\text{gradient}^2}$

⑨ (a) $\frac{1}{V}$ against $\frac{1}{R}$,

(b) Intercept on $\frac{1}{V}$-axis is $\frac{1}{E}$, and the gradient is $\frac{r}{E}$, so $E = \frac{1}{\text{intercept}}$ and $r = \frac{\text{gradient}}{\text{intercept}}$

⑩ 221 ± 8 kPa

⑪ 1.4%

⑫ (a) 1.8% or 2%;
(b) 15.3 ± 0.3 cm^3

⑬ 0.52 ± 0.2 cm^3

Answers to practice questions

① **Model answer**: The resultant force is zero and the resultant moment about any point is zero.

Alternative answer: The [vector] sum of the forces is zero and the clockwise moment about any point is equal to the anticlockwise moment about the same point.

Commentary: Candidates often forget about the moment. If the resultant moment isn't zero, the body will start rotating. It is important that all moments are taken about the same point.

② **Model answer**: A black body is one which absorbs all electromagnetic radiation which is incident upon it.

Commentary: This is the easiest definition. Often candidates mistakenly think that they need to give a definition in terms of the *emission* of radiation, perhaps because a star is clearly radiating. It is possible to give a definition in terms of emission – but it is less satisfactory.

Alternative answer: A black body is one which emits the maximum possible amount of radiation at every wavelength.

Unsatisfactory answer: A black body is one which absorbs all wavelengths [or frequencies] of electromagnetic radiation which are incident upon it.

Commentary: This answer is not credited because it is not clear that <u>all</u> e-m radiation is absorbed – it could be that 50% of the radiation is absorbed at all wavelengths.

③ **Model answer**: A transverse wave is one in which the particle oscillations are at right angles to the direction of propagation of the wave.

Example: Electromagnetic waves / seismic S-waves

A longitudinal wave is one in which the particle oscillations are in line with / parallel to the direction of propagation of the wave.

Example: Sound waves / seismic P-waves

Commentary: The answer needs to make clear which two directions are at right angles, or in line as appropriate. The definition given is not entirely general – it covers the case of a wave which consists of oscillations of a medium. Electromagnetic waves consist of coupled oscillations of electric and magnetic fields rather than particles but the examiners will not expect reference to this.

④ **Model answer**: This means that 5.0 J of energy is transferred per unit of charge [or for every coulomb of charge] which passes through the component.

Less acceptable answer: 5.0 J of energy is converted into heat when 1 C of charge passes through . . . (?)

Commentary: Why is the second answer not as good as the first?

- 'Heat' is itself an energy transfer, so the expression isn't good, but more importantly (for AS) the energy transfer could be to mechanical work, e.g. in a motor.

- The 2nd 'definition' doesn't allow for quantities of charge other than 1 C, while the first one clearly implies that when 2 C of charge passes, 10 J of energy is transferred, etc. This fits in with the unit equivalence $V = J\,C^{-1}$.

⑤ **Model answer**: For a metallic conductor at a constant temperature the current is [directly] proportional to the potential difference.

Commentary: There are two marks – one mark is for the proportionality and the other for the conditions under which it applies.

Unsatisfactory answer: $V = I \times R$ [or expressed in any other way].

Commentary: Why is this not accepted? The equation is just the definition of electrical resistance ['to find the resistance, divide the pd by the current']. It doesn't even state that V and I are proportional – it would need to add that R is a constant. The equation $V = I \times R$ can be used to calculate the resistance of a component for which V and I are not proportional, e.g. a light bulb filament or a diode, although there will be a different answer for different values of V and I.

⑥ **Model answer**: [This applies to superconductors.] As a conductor is cooled, the transition temperature is the temperature at which the resistance suddenly drops to zero.

Less satisfactory answer: This is the temperature, below which a material is superconducting (?).

Unsatisfactory answer: The temperature at which the resistance of a superconductor is zero.

Commentary: The answer needs to make clear:

- There is a sudden change in resistance – the second statement is weak here.

- The zero resistance state is for all temperatures [or at least a range of temperatures] *below* the transition temperature – the third statement suggests it is only zero at that temperature.

⑦ **Model answer**: When two [or more] waves pass through [or exist at] a point, the [total] displacement of the medium at that point is equal to the [vector] sum of the displacements due to the individual waves [at that point].

Commentary: There are two parts to the answer. The first one describes the situation, i.e. it deals with two waves. The second describes how they are combined. The words in square brackets are good to have but are not strictly necessary: if the principle works for two waves, it will hold for three or more; the displacement of the medium must be the total displacement; there is only one way to add displacements, i.e. as vectors!

⑧ **Model answer**: A hadron is a particle which is composed of quarks. ✓

A baryon consists of 3 quarks, e.g. a proton [neutron, delta, Δ^{++}, etc.] ✓

A meson consists of a quark and an antiquark, e.g. a pion [π^+, π^0, etc.]. ✓

Commentary: It is unlikely that an examiner would ask the question in quite this form. Asking for an example of, say, a baryon, means that the examiner must be prepared to accept any out of a vast zoo of baryons, Ω^-, Σ^+, etc. An alternative definition of the hadron is a composite particle which experiences the strong interaction.

⑨ **Model answer**: Multimode dispersion.

Commentary: If you cannot remember the name, give a description in the hope that the mark scheme will allow for it, e.g. in fibres with a wide core, some light rays pass down the middle and others have a zig-zag path and so take different times to reach the other end.

⑩ **Model answer**: 'EMF of 10.0 V' means that 10.0 J of energy is transferred from an external source ✓ per unit charge which passes through the supply ✓.

'PD across its terminals is 9.0 V' means that 9.0 J of energy is transferred to the external circuit ✓ per unit charge which passes through the supply.

Commentary: The unit of both EMF and pd is the volt, which is defined as the joule per coulomb, so the explanation must involve both the energy transfer and the expression 'per unit charge' or 'per coulomb'. The context of the energy transfer needs

to be given to distinguish the two quantities: EMF refers to energy into the electrical system, e.g. from chemical energy in the cell, or mechanical work done on a dynamo; pd refers to the energy provided by the power supply to the external circuit [this is often more accurately described as the 'electrical work done on the external circuit'] per unit charge. In most cases, the examiner will look for the expression 'per unit charge' used correctly at least once in the answer.

Experimental description questions

⑪ **Model answer**:

(a) The resistance of a length of conductor is given by: $R = \dfrac{\rho l}{A}$

So $\rho = \dfrac{RA}{l}$

so the unit of $\rho = \dfrac{\Omega m^2}{m} = \Omega\, m$.

(b) Apparatus required: Ohm-meter, metre rule, micrometer.

Method: Measure the resistance of a length of wire using the ohm-meter. First check the resistance of the ohm-meter leads by touching them together – subtract this from the reading for the resistance of the wire.

Measure the length, l, of the wire using the metre rule.

Measure the diameter, d, of the wire, at several points, using the micrometer, determine the mean value and calculate the cross-sectional area using the equation:

$$A = \frac{\pi d^2}{4}$$

Finally, calculate the resistivity using the equation $\rho = \dfrac{RA}{l}$

Commentary:

(a) The equation given in the data sheet needs to be manipulated so that the resistivity is the subject. The unit equation is written, i.e. the equation with the units of the quantities instead of the quantities themselves. You need to do enough, so the examiner believes you know what you are doing!

(b) The apparatus used is stated. There is no need for a diagram here. The necessary measurements are stated, including avoiding obvious uncertainties, such as the zero-error of the ohm-meter.

How you use the measurements to give the final answer is stated – in this case, how A and, finally, ρ are determined.

⑫ **Model answer:**

The wire is placed into a beaker of water as shown and the beaker heated gradually using a Bunsen burner [on tripod and gauze]. The resistance and temperature readings are taken by removing the Bunsen and stirring [thermometer] to allow the temperature to become uniform and then the readings on the thermometer and resistance meter noted. A series of readings up to about 100°C are obtained. For greater accuracy the resistance of the leads to the coil is measured and subtracted to obtain the resistance of the coil inside the liquid.

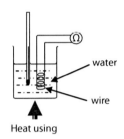

Heat using

Commentary:

The set-up is clear – this helped by a diagram. There is no need to label standard pieces of apparatus [beaker, thermometer, ohm-meter]. The procedure is clear enough for another AS student to follow it.

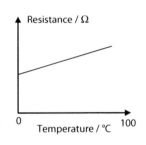

The graph is shown as straight with a non-zero intercept on the resistance axis. In reality it is not exactly straight, but it is very nearly straight over this limited temperature range.

⑬ **Model answer:**

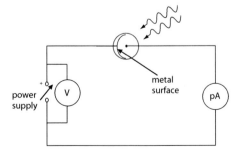

[Note additions to diagram]. The pd of the power supply is increased from zero and the current monitored. As the pd increases, the current drops and the minimum pd, V_s, for which the current is zero is noted. The maximum kinetic energy is eV_s.

Commentary: The three modifications to the circuit – polarity of the supply, variable power supply and voltmeter – are shown. The experimental technique, including the necessary statement, 'starting from zero', is given; the necessary measurement stated and the method of calculation given.

(b) (i) Determine the gradient of the graph – this is the Planck constant.

(b) (ii) Extend the graph until it reaches the vertical axis. The intercept is the negative of the value of the work function, ie intercept $= -\phi$.

Commentary: Note that the command word is 'state' – there is no need for any explanations.

(b) (ii) There is arguably no need for the first sentence but it does make the answer clear – the line could be added to the graph on the question paper. One of the marks is for the 'negative' in the answer. There is an alternative answer, which is 'note the intercept, $f_{threshold}$, on the frequency axis. The work function is $h \times f_{threshold}$'

Questions to test understanding

⑭ **Model answer:**

$$\text{Units of r.h.s.} = \sqrt{\frac{N}{kg\,m^{-1}}}$$

$$= \sqrt{\frac{kg\,m\,s^{-2}}{kg\,m^{-2}}}$$

$$= \sqrt{m^2\,s^{-2}}$$

$$= m\,s^{-1} = \text{units of l.h.s.}$$

So the equation **is** homogeneous, i.e. it is possible in terms of units.

Commentary: The working started with the complicated [right-hand] side, expressed the quantities on that side in terms of their units, and simplified the resulting expression. The resulting expression was shown to be the same as the units of the left-hand side. The use of a single cascade of equations, each starting on a new line, with the equals signs aligned, considerably aids communication.

⑮ **Model answer**:

(a) Initially, the gravitational force is greater than the air resistance and so the skydiver's acceleration is downwards. When the parachute opens, the air resistance becomes much greater. The air resistance, an upwards force, is greater than the downward gravitational force, so the resultant force is upwards and so the acceleration is upwards. As the skydiver's velocity decreases, the air resistance decreases until it equals the force of gravity, so the resultant force and therefore the acceleration becomes zero.

(b) The total area between the time axis and the line gives the velocity. This velocity must be positive (downwards) because the parachutist is moving downwards. QED.

Commentary: In fact, the area for the first 20s will give the first terminal velocity (around 45 m s^{-1} if you want to work it out). The area for the next 17 s is around − 40 m s^{-1}. This means that the final terminal velocity will be around 5 m s^{-1}.

⑯ **Model answer**:

Resistance of parallel combination $= \dfrac{10 \times 15}{10+15} = 6\,\Omega$

Using the potential divider formula:

pd across 12 $\Omega = \dfrac{12}{12+6} \times 9.0\ V = 6.0\ V$

Alternative to the second stage:

Total resistance $= 12 + 6 = 18\,\Omega$

∴ Total current [= current through the 12 Ω resistor]

$= \dfrac{V}{R} = \dfrac{9.0}{18} = 0.5\ A$

∴ pd across 12 V resistor $= IR = 0.5 \times 12 = 6\ V$.

Commentary: Questions like this require repeated use of simple equations, e.g. $V = IR$, to different aspects of the circuit. It is very important to make it clear which components are referred to in your working, hence you need to say, for example, 'resistance of the parallel combination'.

⑰ **Model answer**:

(a) Total resistance in the circuit $= r + R = 0.5 + 12.5 = 13.0\,\Omega$.

∴ Current $= \dfrac{emf}{total\ resistance} = \dfrac{1.5}{13} = 0.115\ A$

(b) Current $= \dfrac{emf}{total\ resistance} = \dfrac{1.5n}{12.5+0.5n}$

If current ≥ 0.6 A; $\dfrac{1.5n}{12.5+0.5n} \geq 0.6$

∴ $1.5n \geq 0.6\,(12.5 + 0.5n)$

[Expanding the bracket] ∴ $1.5n \geq 7.5 + 0.3n$

[Rearranging] ∴ $1.5n - 0.3n \geq 7.5$

i.e. $1.2n \geq 7.5$ so $n \geq 7.5/1.2 = 6.25$.

So the minimum number of cells is 7 [it must be a whole number]

Commentary: The idea that EMF is the 'total voltage' in the circuit is very useful in this type of question.

(b) This is an ideal answer but trial and error is also quite acceptable. If you don't like using the inequality sign [≥] an alternative is to use the equality sign [=], arrive at the answer 6.25 and then make the statement that the smallest whole number which will do is the next one up, i.e. 7.

⑱ **Model answer**:

(a) Rearranging the equation: $k = \dfrac{F}{v^2}$.

So unit of k = N (m s^{-1})$^{-2}$ = N m^{-2} s^2.

(b) (i) The two forces on her are weight (mg downwards) and air resistance upwards:

Resultant force $= 75 \times 9.81 - 0.30 \times 20^2 = 616$ N

(ii) At terminal velocity, resultant force = 0

So $mg = k\,v^2$, i.e. $75 \times 9.81 = 0.3\,v^2$

So $v^2 = 2452.5$, so $v = 49.5$ m s$^{-1} \sim 50$ m s^{-1}.

(iii) **Model answer:** Using the middle value of velocity [40 m s^{-1}] to estimate the resultant force:

Estimated resultant force $= 75 \times 9.81 - 0.30 \times 40^2 = 256$ N

Acceleration $= \dfrac{F}{m} = \dfrac{256}{75} = 3.41$ m s^{-2}.

Time taken $= \dfrac{\text{change in velocity}}{\text{acceleration}} = \dfrac{10}{3.41} \sim 3$ s

Commentary:

(a) 'Show that' means that the working must be clear. In this case, the initial rearranging of the equation followed by the algebra – the examiner must believe you knew what you were doing!

(b) (i) The physical principle of the answer is clear and well expressed. In an exam, full marks would be given for just the final answer [if it were correct!]

(ii) This is a 'show that', so there would be no marks for just stating the final answer – the reasoning must be clear.

(iii) The word 'estimate' does not mean 'guess' – you need to do a calculation with a simplifying assumption. In this case the simplification replaces the varying drag force with a constant typical one from the middle of the velocity range.

⑲ **Model answer**:

In this circuit, the total input voltage, V_{IN} is given by:

$V_{IN} = IR_{Total} = I(R + X)$

$V_{OUT} = IR$ – assuming that the current in the two resistors is the same, i.e. no current is taken by V_{OUT}.

Dividing: $\dfrac{V_{OUT}}{V_{IN}} = \dfrac{IR}{I(R + X)}$

Cancelling by I on the r.h.s.: $\dfrac{V_{OUT}}{V_{IN}} = \dfrac{R}{R + X}$ QED

Commentary: The working clearly uses $V = IR$ twice and, importantly, gives the context for each step – 1st for the two resistors in series and 2nd for resistor R alone. The assumption is clearly given and the cancellation by I explicitly stated.

⑳ **Model answer**:

(a) The current through L_1 splits up equally to pass through L_2 and L_3. This means that L_1 is bright and L_2 and L_3 are dimmer than L_1 and equally bright.

(b) Because one branch of the parallel combination has been removed, the total resistance of the circuit increases. This means that the total current decreases. L_1 is therefore less bright. The current in L_2 is the same as that that in L_1, so these two lamps now have the same brightness, which is greater than the original brightness of L_2.

Commentary:

(a) The explanation is given before the comparison but both parts of the answer are given.

(b) The basis of the answer is clearly stated – the total resistance increases – and its effect on the current and the brightness of the lamps.

PH3 Practical Physics questions

㉑ **Model answer**:

The resolution of the rule is 1 mm but I can read to the nearest 0.5 mm.

Thickness of 500 sheets of paper tightly held = 5.15 ± 0.05 cm.

So the thickness of 1 sheet of paper $= \dfrac{5.15 \pm 0.05}{500}$ cm = 0.0103 ± 0.0001 cm.

The length of the A4 sheets = 29.75 ± 0.05 cm

The width of the A4 sheets = 21.00 ± 0.05 cm

Best estimate of volume = length × width × thickness

= 29.75 cm × 21.00 cm × 0.0103 cm

= 6.4349 cm^3.

The % uncertainty in the thickness of a sheet $p_t = \dfrac{0.0001}{0.0103} \times 100 = 0.97\%$

The % uncertainty in the length of a sheet $p_l = \dfrac{0.05}{29.75} \times 100 = 0.17\%$

The % uncertainty in the width of a sheet $p_w = \dfrac{0.05}{21.00} \times 100 = 0.24\%$

% uncertainty in volume, $p_v = p_l + p_w + p_t$

= 0.17 + 0.24 + 0.97

= 1.4%

∴ uncertainty in volume = 1.4% × 6.435 cm^3 = 0.09 cm^3 [to 1 s.f.]

∴ Volume of a sheet of A4 paper = 6.43 ± 0.09 cm^3

Commentary:

The resolution of the measuring instrument is stated and the claim that the experimenter can read to half the resolution – this justifies the subsequent work. There is no need for repeat readings here because:

- the use of 500 sheets is essentially the same as a repeat reading for thickness, and

- length and width of the paper are very tightly controlled.

The ±0.05 cm is therefore accepted as the uncertainty in a measurement. Note that the thickness of a sheet is left in cm rather than mm because it has to be combined with the length and thickness which are both in cm. It would have been equally possible to express all three quantities in mm.

The volume of a sheet is calculated by length × width × thickness. It would have been equally satisfactory to determine the volume of the block of paper and to divide that by 500. Extra significant figures should be left at this stage – it is not good practice to round more than once.

The percentage uncertainties for length, width and thickness are calculated and, again, an extra significant figure is retained. The absolute uncertainty is then calculated and, as this is the end of the calculation, it is quoted to 1 s.f. [the calculation gives 0.09009 cm³]. Because the significant figure in the uncertainty is in the 2nd decimal place, the figure for volume is rounded to 2 decimal places. If the entire calculation had been carried out in mm, the final answer would have been expressed as 6430 ± 90 mm³.

㉒ **Model answer:**

(a) and (b) – see the completed table.

R/Ω	I/A	$\dfrac{1}{I(A)}$
1.5	0.866	1.15(5)
2.2	0.656	1.52(4)
3.3	0.441	2.27
3.8	0.388	2.58
4.7	0.313	3.19
5.6	0.271	3.69

(c)

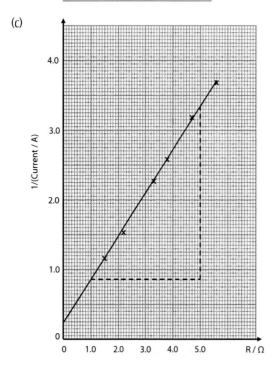

(d) The equation suggests that a graph of $1/I$ against R should be a straight line with a positive gradient of $1/E$ and a positive intercept on the vertical axis of r/E. The graph **is** a straight line with a positive gradient., with the points showing very little scatter. The intercept on the $1/I$ axis is positive [+0.23 A⁻¹] so both aspects of the graph support the theoretical equation, with E and r being constant.

(e) The gradient of the graph =

$$\frac{(3.34-0.86)}{(5.00-1.00)}=\frac{2.48}{4.00}=0.620$$

The gradient is $1/E$ ∴ $E=\dfrac{1}{0.620}=1.61$ V

The intercept is r/E so $r=1.61\times0.23=0.37\ \Omega$

Commentary:

(a) The resistance values are as given and the current readings as appeared on the ammeter which was set on the 2 A range.

(b) The 1/current values are given to 3 figures apart from the first two, for which the fourth figure is given in brackets. This is because the first significant figure is 1, so giving the figure to 3 s.f. would increase the uncertainty in the data well above that for current.

(c) The graph has labelled axes which exploit the full range of the graph paper. The scales are uniform. The units are given. The points are plotted within half a square. A reasonable line is drawn consistent with the data. The line is extended to meet the vertical axis – which is required later on.

(d) The various aspects of the line are commented on: straight, positive gradient and intercept. They are compared to the prediction. The degree of scatter is commented on, which is important as, if there had been a large degree of scatter, the strength of the confirmation of the relationship would have been lower. There is no requirement to state the value of the intercept here, but it is used in part (e).

(e) The gradient is determined using a large triangle on the graph – the triangle is drawn in, helping the examiner to see what the candidate has done. Note that it is not necessary to include units on the gradient.

The gradient and intercept are used correctly to determine E and r.

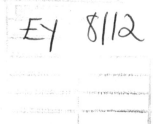

EY 8112

Lightning Source UK Ltd.
Milton Keynes UK
UKOW010319020612

193790UK00002B/5/P

9 781908 682048